KIT CARSON, *Stevenson*
LOTTA CRABTREE, *Place*
MERIWETHER LEWIS, *Bebenroth*
NARCISSA WHITMAN, *Warner*
SACAGAWEA, *Seymour*
SAM HOUSTON, *Stevenson*
SIMON KENTON, *Wilkie*
TECUMSEH, *Stevenson*
WILL CLARK, *Wilkie*
WILLIAM FARGO, *Wilkie*
WILLIAM HENRY HARRISIN, *Peckham*
ZEB PIKE, *Stevenson*

THE
NATION
DIVIDED

ABE LINCOLN, *Stevenson*
BEDFORD FORREST, *Parks*
CLARA BARTON, *Stevenson*
DAVID FARRAGUT, *Long*
HARRIET BEECHER STOWE, *Widdemer*
JEB STUART, *Winders*
JEFF DAVIS, *de Grummond and Delaune*
JULIA WARD HOWE, *Wagoner*
MARY TODD LINCOLN, *Wilkie*
RAPHAEL SEMMES, *Snow*
ROBERT E. LEE, *Monsell*
TOM JACKSON, *Monsell*
U. S. GRANT, *Stevenson*

RECONSTRUCTION
and
EXPANSION

ALECK BELL, *Widdemer*
ALLAN PINKERTON, *Borland and Speicher*
BOOKER T. WASHINGTON, *Stevenson*
CYRUS McCORMICK, *Dobler*
FRANCES WILLARD, *Mason*
JOHN WANAMAKER, *Burt*
LEW WALLACE, *Schaaf*
LOUISA ALCOTT, *Wagoner*
LUTHER BURBANK, *Burt*
MARIA MITCHELL, *Melin*
MARK TWAIN, *Mason*
MARY MAPES DODGE, *M...*
SITTING BULL, *Stevenson*
SUSAN ANTHONY, *Monsell*
TOM EDISON, *Guthridge*

TURN
OF THE
CENTURY

ANNIE OAKLEY, *Wilson*
DAN BEARD, *Mason*
ELIZABETH BLACKWELL, *Henry*
GEORGE CARVER, *Stevenson*
GEORGE DEWEY, *Long*
GEORGE EASTMAN, *Henry*
JAMES WHITCOMB RILEY, *Mitchell*
JANE ADDAMS, *Wagoner*
JOHN PHILIP SOUSA, *Weil*
J. STERLING MORTON, *Moore*
JULIETTE LOW, *Higgins*
KATE DOUGLAS WIGGIN, *Mason*
KATHARINE LEE BATES, *Myers*
LILIUOKALANI, *Newman*
THE RINGLING BROTHERS, *Burt*
ROBERT PEARY, *Clark*
TEDDY ROOSEVELT, *Parks*
WALTER REED, *Higgins*
WILBUR AND ORVILLE WRIGHT,
  Stevenson
WILL AND CHARLIE MAYO,
  Hammontree

IN RECENT
YEARS

ALBERT EINSTEIN, *Hammontree*
AMELIA EARHART, *Howe*
A. P. GIANNINI, *Hammontree*
BABE RUTH, *Van Riper, Jr.*
CARL BEN EIELSON, *Myers
  and Burnett*
ERNIE PYLE, *Wilson*
FRANKLIN ROOSEVELT, *Weil*
HENRY FORD, *Aird and Ruddiman*
... *Riper, Jr.*
... *erson*
... *Van Riper, Jr.*
... *Riper, Jr.*
... HOLMES, JR.,
... *Van Riper, Jr.*
... *Weddle*
... *an Riper, Jr.*
WOODROW WILSON, *Monsell*

John Paul Jones

Salt-Water Boy

Illustrated by William Moyers

John Paul
Jones

Salt-Water Boy

By Dorothea J. Snow

THE **BOBBS-MERRILL** COMPANY, INC.
A SUBSIDIARY OF HOWARD W. SAMS & CO., INC.
Publishers • INDIANAPOLIS • NEW YORK

LIBRARY OF CONGRESS CATALOG CARD NUMBER: 62-12693

PRINTED IN THE UNITED STATES OF AMERICA

For my brother, William E. (Bill) Johnston, whose knowledge of the seas and the ships that have sailed them aided immeasurably in the writing of this book

Illustrations

Numerous smaller illustrations

Contents

 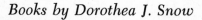

Books by Dorothea J. Snow

ELI WHITNEY: BOY MECHANIC
JOHN PAUL JONES: SALT-WATER BOY
RAPHAEL SEMMES: TIDEWATER BOY
SAMUEL MORSE: INQUISITIVE BOY

★ ★ # Jᴏʜɴ Pᴀᴜʟ Jᴏɴᴇꜱ

Salt-Water Boy

A Head on His Shoulders

It was a spring morning in Scotland in 1755. The sun was shining brightly on the waters of the Firth of Solway.

On a small island in the middle of the firth, a man and a boy worked busily in the gardens of the Earl of Selkirk.

The earl owned the island and the big, gray stone castle there. The castle had been the home of the clan of Selkirk for centuries.

A gardener's shears bit into one of the shrubs of a hedge that lined a graveled path leading to the castle.

Seven-year-old Johnny Paul followed as his

Uncle George walked down the hedgerow trimming each shrub. The cuttings flew. Johnny picked them up and tossed them into a two-wheeled cart that stood in the narrow path.

Johnny worked eagerly, hoping that his uncle would notice how fast he could work. Johnny wanted very much to please him. "If I can please Uncle George, perhaps he will let me come back to help him again," he thought.

Work meant money, and money would buy food to eat and clothes to wear. Money was scarce in the Paul household. "I'll give the money that I earn today to Mother. How pleased she will be." Johnny was warmed by the thought that he would be able to help his family.

He couldn't help grinning. "How surprised Father will be!" he thought. His brothers Robert and Albert, would be amazed. None thought that he was big enough to earn money.

Johnny was very small for his age, but he

wanted to be big and _strong_ and husky! He sighed longingly, "I might as well wish for the moon," he thought. "I'll never be husky."

"You're a mite small to help in the garden," Uncle George had said to him when he begged to come along. "I guess, though, you can help a little by picking up the clippings which I trim from the hedges. One thing is mighty certain. You won't have far to reach in picking them up, because you're so close to the ground."

Uncle George moved from shrub to shrub. Johnny made sure that the ground beneath the bushes was clean and tidy. "Has Uncle George noticed how clean the ground is?" he wondered.

Johnny wished that he could do something to make Uncle George notice his work. "If only I could trim a shrub!" he thought.

It looked easy. Just snip a little off here, a little off there. Soon Uncle George had shaped a bush to look like a big green bell.

13

Johnny looked across the path. There he saw a row of shrubs, shaped like peacocks, strutting along its edge. Not far away was a hedge in which the plants were clipped to look like balls.

Trimming was easy. Johnny was sure of that.

He saw an extra pair of shears lying on the ground. Uncle George was out of sight behind one of the shrubs. He couldn't see what Johnny was doing.

Johnny picked up the shears. He headed for a hedge that grew around a small pool.

He stood before the hedge. "How should I trim these shrubs?" he said to himself. "Shall I shape them to look like balls, or maybe cones?"

Then Johnny had an idea. "Frogs! Frogs by a pool would be just right! I'll trim that hedge to look like a row of frogs!"

Johnny set right to work. The clippings flew. "This is fun," he smiled. Johnny liked doing things all by himself. He liked being alone.

A lock of dark hair worked itself out from beneath his tam-o'-shanter. It swung back and forth as he ran first to one side and then to the other side of the shrub. His smoky eyes glowed. "How surprised and pleased Uncle George will be when he sees what a good hedge trimmer I am," he declared.

Johnny heard footsteps on the path behind him. "It's Uncle George! Oh, why didn't he wait until I finished trimming my first shrub?" he moaned. He whirled around quickly.

"How do you like it, Unc—" Johnny stopped short. It wasn't Uncle George who stood behind him, but a strange redheaded boy. The strange boy was about his own age, but bigger, much bigger than he was.

Johnny disliked the boy at once. Johnny didn't care much for other boys and girls his own age, especially bigger ones.

"It looks awful," the stranger remarked.

Johnny clenched his fist. "It does not!" he answered hotly, thrusting his small dark face forward. "I know how to trim a shrub!"

"Trim a shrub!" mocked the redheaded boy squinting again at the shrub. "Were you trimming it? Ruining it I'd say."

Anger turned Johnny's face a dull red. "I'm not ruining this shrub!" he cried. "I'm trimming it to look like a frog, and a frog it will look like when I'm through."

Johnny turned his back on the boy. "I wish that mean boy would go away," he muttered.

"Frog!" the boy sneered back. "It'll be a funny-looking frog!"

Johnny didn't answer.

"My grandfather will want to see that shrub," the voice mocked.

"Your grandfather?" asked Johnny. "Who is your grandfather?"

"The Earl of Selkirk, that's who!"

Johnny whirled and stared. This was the earl's grandson. He certainly didn't want to quarrel with this boy.

The boy made a face. "What made you think that you could trim a shrub?" he asked. "Why, you're just a little shrimp!"

Johnny sizzled. "I don't care if your grandfather is an earl. You can't call me a shrimp." He threw the shears on the ground and started after the boy.

The boy grinned at him. This was just what he wanted Johnny to do. The boy looked back over his shoulder and cried, "You'll need longer legs than you have now to catch me."

That was true. His longer legs kept him well ahead of Johnny.

Johnny tried and tried. He chased the young lord up one path and down another, but he could not catch him.

Then it happened. The strange boy stumbled

and fell flat on his face. Johnny pounded upon him at once, his small fists flying.

"So, I'm a shrimp and I can't trim a hedge," said Johnny. He was determined to show this ugly boy that he wasn't afraid.

The big boy started to fight back, and it was then Johnny began to fight a losing battle. His fists semed to bounce right off the big boy's body. The big boy's fists hit Johnny hard, but he kept right on fighting.

Over and over the boys rolled with legs and arms flying wildly. Johnny landed a lucky punch on the other boy's nose, but still he was beaten. Finally the big boy sat on him, holding one of Johnny's arms in one hand and one of his legs in the other.

"Give up?" the young lord grinned. His red hair was tousled and his fine blue woolen coat was torn. The white ruffle at his neck was dirty, too, but he looked happy.

"Give up," Johnny muttered.

The young lord rose and brushed himself off. Johnny got up, too, but he didn't wait to brush the dirt from his coarse woolen shirt and trousers. He couldn't keep back the tears, but he wasn't going to let that mean redheaded lord see him cry!

Without saying a word, Johnny hurried back to his frog shrub beside the pool.

NOT SO BAD TO BE LITTLE

Johnny found Uncle George standing before the shrub. His face brightened. So Uncle George had noticed it after all!

The brightness in his face faded fast, however, when he heard Uncle George speak angrily. "Did you do this, young man?"

"Y-y-yes, sir," Johnny stammered.

Johnny looked at the shrub for the first time

from a distance. "It doesn't look a bit like a frog!" he thought. "I *have* ruined it."

Panic ran through Johnny. He wished that he had never touched the shrub. The earl knew and loved every growing thing in the gardens. Johnny was the gardener's nephew, and he had ruined a fine yew tree!

"The earl will speak to Uncle George and all because of me," Johnny thought.

Uncle George would never let him help again, of that he was certain. Once more he felt like bursting into tears, but he didn't. He knew that real boys didn't cry, not even little boys, but his spirits sank lower. He remembered that it was because he was little that the earl's grandson had beaten him. "Why, oh, why, did I have to be so little?"

"I thought it was such a fine idea," he muttered, "to have a frog beside a pool."

Uncle George turned toward Johnny. "A frog

did you say?" His voice softened. "Get my shears, son," he said kindly. "Perhaps I can help you with this problem."

Johnny ran for the shears and the cart.

Uncle George set to work at once. Johnny picked up the clippings.

Now and then Uncle George stopped. He would step back and squint at the shrub. Then he would start clipping again.

Johnny watched his uncle shape the shrub. Soon it began to look like a frog.

"There," said Uncle George after a final squint. "I guess it's all right now."

Johnny was glad. He was so glad that the shrub wasn't ruined after all. It really looked like a frog now, a big, fat, green frog.

"Will Uncle George ever let me be his helper again?" Johnny thought of the money and hoped that he would be asked to help many times.

Footsteps sounded in the path again. Uncle

George and Johnny turned around. There stood
the Earl of Selkirk, and he was smiling.

"A frog!" he cried. "A hedge of frogs beside
a pool. How clever!"

Uncle George beamed with pride. He waved his shears toward Johnny.

" 'Twas Johnny's idea," he bragged.

The earl turned to Johnny. He laid a kindly hand on the boy's shoulder.

"You may be small, lad," he boomed, "but you have a head on your shoulders."

Turning to Uncle George, the earl said, "A fine helper you have here."

Uncle George nodded. "Indeed he is."

Johnny could have danced for joy. Uncle George thought that he was a good helper.

The earl strolled on. Johnny and his uncle returned to their work. Johnny sang gaily.

"Perhaps being little isn't so bad after all. Not if a boy has a head on his shoulders!" he murmured happily.

Dark of the Moon

"ALBERT! Robert! John! Breakfast!"

Johnny and his brothers rolled out of bed. Their room was very dark. There was no light shining through its tiny window for it was too early in the morning.

The boys hurriedly dressed. They washed in the iron basin by the back door. Then they went to the rough table by the fireplace. Their mother was putting their food on the table as they arrived.

By the flickering light of the peat fire on the hearth, the boys could see that their father had already sat down to breakfast.

They all sighed in relief. The family had a rule that anyone who was late to breakfast could not have even his bowl of oatmeal.

Mrs. Paul's eyes went from one to the other of her boys. They rested on Johnny, her youngest son. Johnny looked just like his mother who was small and dark. He carried himself with the same fierce pride.

Mrs. Paul smiled at Johnny. Johnny grinned back. He glowed inside for he knew what that smile meant. Mother, too, hoped that he'd get to go fishing today.

Johnny liked to fish even more than he liked to help his Uncle George and more than he liked to earn money. He loved the water and enjoyed being near it.

"You'll be sprouting fins, son, if you don't watch out," his father once remarked after seeing Johnny swim.

Johnny knew that his mother could always

use the fish he caught. Fish went a long way
toward making up a good meal.

Uncle George didn't need Johnny today, so he
was going fishing, he hoped.

The last of the oatmeal was eaten. Mr. Paul
rose from the table. He went to the door and
looked out.

"Today will be a sunny day," he declared.
Turning to Albert and Robert, he said, "So you
will plant the potato patch today."

"Hooray!" cried the two older boys. They
hugged each other and danced about. "No school
today! Hooray!"

"Shhhh!" Mrs. Paul cautioned softly. "You'll
waken little Lisbeth."

Mother was too late. Lisbeth was already
awake. She was sitting up in her trundle bed,
clapping her chubby hands together.

"See!" Albert laughed. "Sister is glad, too,
that we don't have to go to school today."

It seemed that Lisbeth was indeed glad. She slid out of the low bed and toddled over to where they all stood. She crowed and gurgled at the boys. At fifteen months of age, Lisbeth was a great favorite with her brothers. How she loved to follow them around.

Johnny grinned at his brothers' delight. He knew how much they hated to go to school. They would much rather work in the fields any time than go to school.

"Potatoes! What are potatoes?" Johnny wondered. He knew only that they were a kind of food. The Earl of Selkirk had a patch of potatoes every year.

Father picked up his rough plaid. The morning air was always chilly on the moors, or rolling hills, around the Paul home.

"Mother will show you how to cut up the seed potatoes," Father said. He threw the plaid about his shoulders. "We should have a good crop this year. It is the dark of the moon. That is just the right time to plant things that grow underground."

"Potatoes will be a welcome change from turnips," said Mrs. Paul smiling.

"They will indeed," Mr. Paul agreed. "The master's cook gave me one of the potatoes that she had roasted in the ashes of the hearth. It was very tasty. The master says it is high time we Scotsmen stop thinking of potatoes as being poisonous roots."

Mr. Paul said good-by to his family. He left for work. Like his brother, George, he was a gardener. He cared for the lawns and gardens of William Craik, a well-to-do tradesman. Mr. Paul's wages were very small, but he was allowed to live in this two-room stone cottage without paying rent. The cottage was located on a few acres of land on which he raised food for his growing family.

Mr. Paul reached the lane and stopped. He turned to Johnny and said, "You must help plant the potatoes. You can drop in the seed."

Johnny's heart sank. The first rays of the sun were pinking the sky. "It's a perfect day for fishing, and I have to help Albert and Robert plant potatoes," he moaned.

FAIRY KNOLL

Mrs. Paul showed the boys how to cut up the old potatoes for seed.

"Let's not ruin a single eye," she said. "With luck every eye will become a potato plant. On each plant several potatoes will grow."

The boys understood. Anything that could make a good meal for the family was too precious to lose. They cut up the potatoes so that they would not harm a single eye.

Johnny looked at one of the tiny sprouts on a

wrinkled potato. "This doesn't look like an eye to me!" he thought to himself.

He held up the potato.

"What has a dozen eyes yet cannot see?" he chanted gaily. "If you know the answer, tell me please."

"Not a bad riddle, Johnny," said his mother laughing.

She smiled at him, pleased. Johnny liked to make up rhymes and jingles. He liked to hear his mother read poetry. This pleased her greatly for she loved poetry, too.

"Doesn't anybody know the answer?" Johnny inquired of his brothers.

"If you didn't have a potato in your hand," said Robert, "I might not."

Not long afterward the boys headed for the potato patch. Albert and Robert had already plowed it and made it ready for planting.

Albert and Robert walked fast. Johnny poked

along. He was in no hurry to reach that patch. Besides, he liked his own company. He lagged behind others whenever he could.

Johnny looked down the hillside. At the bottom of the hill sparkled the waters of the firth, the long, narrow bay that came clear in from the sea. Johnny knew that far down the firth, on the seacoast, lay the town of Whitehaven.

Johnny had never been to Whitehaven. He had never seen the open sea. Yet he knew that it was a big body of water. He knew, too, that somewhere beyond the sea lay the land called America. His big brother William and his sisters Janet and Mary lived there.

Johnny wasn't thinking of America right now. Nor was he thinking about the sea. He was admiring the blue waters of the firth.

"I wish I were down there fishing," he thought longingly.

He looked down at his basket of seed potatoes. He breathed a deep sigh. "What a dull day this is going to be!" he muttered.

The boys reached the path. They dug rows of holes into which they dropped the seed. They covered the seed with dirt.

Up and down. Up and down the rows they worked. Johnny grew tired. He stopped for a few minutes to rest.

Before him was a little hill, a knoll, right in the middle of the potato patch! On top of it a twisted old tree grew. There was a thicket of weeds and bushes around it. Such an untidy spot looked out of place in the neat field.

Johnny knew why the hill was there. It was a fairy knoll. Everyone knew that a fairy knoll was a place where fairies came at night to sing and dance and make merry.

"I wonder what would happen," he said aloud, "if I planted a potato beneath that tree." Albert and Robert stared at him, open-mouthed.

"Well, aren't you the bold one!"

"The fairies would bewitch it, of course!" they chorused.

"Like the bean in the story 'Jack and the Beanstalk'?" Johnny asked excitedly.

"Most likely."

Johnny's lively mind started working. He believed in fairies. They were said to be kindly little people unless they were crossed. Some people had seen fairies, or so they said. Johnny hadn't, but he'd like to see some. And he wasn't afraid of crossing the little folk.

Johnny dropped one potato seed into the pocket of his jacket.

FUNNY LITTLE FAIRY

Evening came. The potato patch was planted. Every seed, except the one in Johnny's pocket, had been planted in the warm brown earth.

34

Bedtime came early. Johnny had a hard time keeping awake as he lay in bed. He waited until Robert and Albert were asleep. When his Mother and Father stirred no more, he slipped quietly out of bed.

Noiselessly he dressed. He tiptoed to the door of the room.

The fire in the fireplace had burned down to a red glow. When everyone seemed to be asleep, Johnny slipped out into the dark night as silently as a falling feather.

He did not see two big, dark eyes watching every move he made.

It was almost black outside. It was still, too, except for the soft lapping of the waters of the firth not far away.

Johnny looked around. He wasn't afraid. He knew that big shape ahead was the cow house, the byre, where the cows and the sheep slept. He knew that weird, snakelike shadow was the stone

fence. "How different everything looks at night," he thought.

"Fairies! What kind of creatures are they?" Johnny wondered. "I shall find out for myself," he whispered. He went on boldly.

Johnny found the stile and climbed over it. Soon he stood beneath the twisted tree.

He peered about. In spite of the darkness, he could see that there were no fairies here yet, but he was certain that they would come. Johnny dropped to his knees and started to dig in the earth. When the hole was deep enough he dropped in the potato seed.

With pounding heart, he hid behind the tree and waited anxiously.

"How will the fairies come?" he wondered. "Will they come in tiny golden chariots drawn by fireflies? Or will they be treading the air with their magic pointed slippers? Or perhaps they will fly in on gossamer wings."

Other strange thoughts went through Johnny's mind as he waited. "What will the fairies do to me? Will they bewitch the potato? Will huge green leaves on a thick stalk pop from the ground? Will the stalk grow and grow until it is lost in the sky? Will I be able to climb it? Will I, too, find a giant and a castle and a treasure in the clouds?

"Why don't they come?" Johnny whispered impatiently. He shifted his weight. His legs began to ache from crouching down so long.

He waited and waited. No fairies came. Nothing happened to the potato seed. In spite of himself, Johnny dozed off.

He awoke with a start. "What was that noise?" He wondered if the fairies were coming. "Why yes, here they come now!" A tiny, white-clad figure was coming across the field!

Johnny stared. A fairy! A tiny, white-robed fairy was coming straight toward him. Johnny licked his lips. "What will happen now?" he wondered anxiously.

The figure was close to the knoll now.

"Yonny!" it called. Johnny almost fell backward. That white-clad figure was Lisbeth in her nightgown. She had followed him.

"I'd best get you back home," Johnny said with disappointment.

Hastily he dug up the potato seed. Lisbeth was beside him now. She helped him. He stuck the seed back into his pocket. It wouldn't do to let Albert or Robert find it there. They would only laugh at his foolishness.

Johnny picked up Lisbeth and staggered back home. He wondered how she had got across the stile, but babies could do a lot, he knew, when they made up their minds to it.

Somehow he put Lisbeth back in bed without waking anyone. Knowing her Johnny was back in the house, she went to sleep right away.

Soon Johnny was snuggled beneath his own covers. He was very disappointed. After all that trouble he did not see a single fairy. "Why didn't they come?"

All at once Johnny noticed that there was no light shining through his window. He suddenly remembered that his father had said it was the dark of the moon.

"That's it!" he sat up excitedly. "The fairies didn't come tonight because it's the dark of the moon. Fairies come out only on moonlight nights!"

He soon fell fast asleep, his belief in fairies as strong as ever.

Luck for a
Laddie

ONE MORNING Johnny was churning butter for his mother. He lifted the dasher and pushed it down. Up and down, up and down! "The butter is a long time coming," he sighed.

Johnny frowned. Today he could not help his Uncle George in order to earn money. He wouldn't be able to go fishing either for it was raining very hard outside.

Johnny stopped churning.

He stuck his hand into his pocket and brought out a limp, withered stalk of heather. Heather grew thickly on the Scottish moors. Usually the flowers of the heather plant were purple in color.

This was a special sprig of heather. It had white instead of purple blossoms.

"A sprig of white heather brings the finder luck," his mother had said.

Johnny looked at the heather, a disappointed glint in his eyes. "You've brought me no luck so far," he said. "Else why would I be churning butter instead of earning money or fishing?" He stuck the heather back into his pocket.

Still it rained.

For a while that morning Johnny stirred pudding in the iron kettle hanging over the fire. He didn't mind doing that because pudding smelled so good while it was cooking.

Then he had combed out wool for his mother to spin. A regular comb would not get the snarls out. He had to use a tool called a carder. It wasn't any fun drawing chunks of wool over its scratchy teeth, but this was the only way to untangle the wool.

"You'll soon be big enough to card wool," he told Lisbeth. "You have to be careful not to scratch your fingers though. See?"

Johnny showed his little sister how to do it properly. Lisbeth grabbed a piece of wool and pulled it roughly over the carder, scratching her finger as she did so.

Mrs. Paul's hands were flying as she busily used the spinning wheel. Lisbeth decided that she'd help her mother with the spinning.

Johnny started to churn again. At the same time he watched his mother. The thread she was spinning would be woven into a coarse cloth, a plain-colored cloth. From this cloth Mrs. Paul would make Johnny's first new suit. He would wear the suit when he started to school soon. The cloth would not make a nice looking suit, but Johnny knew that it would wear well.

"I'll probably hate school, too," thought Johnny. Up and down went the dasher. "I wish

I could finish the rhyme that's been skittering around in my mind all morning," he thought.

His thoughts kept skipping around. He thought of his little pile of coins. Each day that he helped his Uncle George he would give his earnings to his mother, and each time she would give one coin back to him. Johnny had several coins now. "How shall I spend them?" he wondered to himself.

Johnny worked at the churn. He grinned. He had finally finished the skittering jingle. With twinkling eyes he looked at his mother. In a sing-song voice he piped:

"Oh, My mother is a Highlander
And my father is a Lowlander.
Now just what does that make me?

A low Highlander
Or a high Lowlander?
If you know the answer, please tell me."

44

Mother turned from her spinning wheel.
"That is a fair jingle, Johnny," she said. Then
she added, "And a hard riddle to answer."

Johnny didn't care about the answer. His

mother had come from the Highlands, the mountainous part of Scotland. His father had come from the Lowlands, the flat, level valleys south of the mountains. The Highlanders were a fierce, warlike people. The Lowlanders were a peaceful, easygoing lot. His mother and father were different in speech and ways, but Johnny loved them both just the same.

Suddenly, the butter came. And just as suddenly, the sun came out.

Johnny ran to the door. Excitedly he turned, and asked, "May I?"

Mrs. Paul smiled. "Yes, you may go fishing, if you like. Take this to Grandfather MacDuff first," she said as she took a small jar from a shelf above the fireplace. "Tell him it will help his aching joints."

Johnny took the jar. He knew what was in it. It held a thick syrupy ointment made of fifteen kinds of roots, leaves, and flowers boiled in honey.

It also contained the dried bodies of a number of bees. Johnny believed that his mother's medicines were as good as any made by the village druggist.

Johnny started for the door. He stopped and turned. "Albert and Robert must be very angry by now, Mother."

"Most likely," Mrs. Paul replied, "but they might as well be in school. The fields are much too wet to work in."

"I'm glad the firth isn't too wet to fish in," he said and left.

Johnny got his fishing pole and bait. With them in one hand and the little earthen jar in the other, he started down the lane.

As he went toward his favorite fishing spot, he sang softly:

"I'm a-going fishing,
    I'm a-going fishing,
        I'm a-going fishing in the firth;

To catch a big, fat salmon,
    To catch a big, fat salmon,
        For Mother dear to roast upon the hearth."

All alone and going fishing! "Lucky, lucky me," he thought.

He patted the sprig of white heather he was carrying in his pocket.

GOOD LUCK OR BAD LUCK?

Johnny reached the village of Arbigland. The town's main street was a long narrow lane lined on both sides with tiny stone cottages and several shops.

Johnny finally reached his destination, a pier which went far out into the water. Some fishing shacks were built on it. There were several fishing boats tied to it, too.

Women were busy laying fish out on the hillside to dry. On sunny days the hillside was covered with drying fish. Johnny sniffed deeply. He liked the smell of drying fish.

Some of the fishing boats were going out to sea. "I'll stop to watch them for just a few minutes. Then I'll take the jar of ointment to Grandfather MacDuff," he murmured.

"Morning, Johnny," said one stout fisherman, grinning at him. "Think you'll get a good haul today?"

"Where do you sell all your fish, Johnny?" asked another.

All the fishermen knew this boy who came so often to fish from the pier. Johnny was used to their teasing.

"My mother gets all the fish I catch," he said smacking his lips. "Mmmmmmm! Does she know how to cook them, too."

"Some day I'll have a boat of my own," he added. "Then I'll fish with a net and catch a lot of fish. I'll make a lot of money, too."

"Yes, you'll get rich a-fishing," said one of the men dryly.

"Let's shove off," said another fisherman to the boy standing beside him.

Johnny wished that he could go out fishing with one of them. Fishermen paid their helpers in money as well as in fish. Johnny liked money. However, none of the fishermen wanted to take along so small a lad.

The fishermen made lots of money, Johnny knew that. They received many coins for the dried, salted fish they took to Whitehaven.

"Someday I'll have a boat and fish with a net. I'll sell fish to the English, too, and earn a great deal of money." To fish and earn money at the same time seemed like the perfect life to young Johnny Paul.

Johnny walked a little farther out on the pier. He passed another fisherman coiling a length of heavy hemp rope.

The fisherman straightened up. He said, "There goes Old Tom MacKenzie bound for another good haul."

Johnny turned eagerly. It was always a treat to see Old Tom MacKenzie's yawl go out or come in. It was the neatest, trimmest craft harbored at the village of Arbigland.

Another fisherman was standing near by. He said, "Seems like owning a craft like that would sweeten a man's disposition, doesn't it?"

The first fisherman went back to coiling his rope. "Seems like," he said, "but it hasn't helped Old Tom's disposition. He's the crabbiest, sourest man I ever did see!"

Johnny had heard that before. He walked to the end of the pier. He watched until Old Tom's yawl was out of sight.

He sat down and put the little jar of muscle ointment beside him. He threw his line into the water. "I will take the ointment to Grandpa later," he said to himself. "I want to watch the boats and fish a while."

All alone and fishing with a warm sun on his back, Johnny sighed happily. He was doing what he liked to do best.

"What are you doing? Fishing?" came a familiar voice from behind him.

Johnny knew to whom that voice belonged. It had spoken from behind him the last time he heard it, too. "What made you think you could trim a shrub, you little shrimp?" the voice had said to him then.

Johnny turned. Yes, he was right. The speaker was the mean redheaded Thomas Selkirk.

"Of course I'm fishing," Johnny replied sourly, as he turned his back to his unwelcome visitor.

Thomas Selkirk sat down beside Johnny on the pier. "Grandpa came to the village," he said airily, "to have his musket fixed. I came along with him."

Johnny didn't like this boy, even if his grand-father was an earl. Still, Johnny knew that he had to be polite.

"Is your grandpa going hunting?" Johnny asked the young lord.

Thomas leaned over. He stuck the toe of one of his boots in the water.

"No," Thomas replied. "He just wants to be sure it is working all right in case he should ever have to use it. Your grandpa is repairing it for him."

Of course, Johnny knew that. His Grandfather MacDuff was the only gunsmith in the village. "My grandfather can fix any kind of musket," he boasted proudly.

"Your grandfather used to be an armorer, didn't he?" Thomas asked. "He has a suit of armor in his shop. I know because I saw it."

Johnny turned back to his fishing. He wished this boy would go away and leave him alone.

Couldn't he see that he wasn't welcome? "Grand-father made that suit when he was a young man," Johnny replied as he yanked on his line. There was nothing on the end of it. "The lord it was made for died before he could claim it."

Johnny looked at the little jar of ointment beside him. "Perhaps I should take it to Grand-father MacDuff now." he thought.

"I know a better place to fish," said Thomas. "Come on, let's try it."

Johnny didn't want to go. He would much rather fish by himself right where he was. How-ever, he couldn't be rude to an earl's grandson, even if he didn't like the boy. He sighed deeply and went with Thomas.

The boys skirted the edge of the village. They came to a brook that flowed into the firth. On its banks grew a few scrubby pine trees. Big and little boulders lay about as thought care-lessly tossed there by some giant hand.

Thomas found a place. He told Johnny, "This place is alive with fish."

Johnny set the earthen jar on a rock. He threw out his line.

"Oh, that isn't the way to do it," said Thomas. "Let me show you." He took the pole from Johnny's hand. Johnny was beginning to like this boy less and less.

Thomas threw out the line. As he did so, he brushed against the jar and knocked it off the rock. It fell heavily on another rock and broke. The medicine oozed out slowly.

Both boys watched in horror. "I'm sorry!" cried Thomas. "I'm so sorry!"

Johnny didn't say a word. He knew he had been right. "It is better to do things alone. If I had been alone this never would have happened." He jumped up. As he did so, he slipped and fell into the brook.

Johnny came out of the water dripping wet.

"Why, oh, why didn't I take that ointment to Grandfather first thing?" he moaned. "Then I wouldn't have met this awful boy again."

Johnny grabbed his fishing pole. Instantly, he started for home.

"You aren't cross, are you?" came Thomas' anxious voice.

Johnny gritted his teeth. "Cross! Why should I be cross?" he growled. Nevertheless, Johnny was angry. He was so angry that he could chew nails. "I hope I never see that Thomas Selkirk again," he muttered aloud.

Something was scratching Johnny's leg. He thrust one hand into the pocket of his soaked trousers and found the sprig of white heather. He smiled grimly. "Luck?" he muttered. "This has brought me luck all right. Bad luck!"

Still, no Scottish lad ever throws away a token of luck. Johnny returned the scratchy sprig to his pocket.

Bad-Luck
Thomas

"No, Johnny," said Mrs. Paul firmly. "You cannot go with Uncle George today. Nor can you go fishing. You must gather herbs and roots and flowers. Because of your carelessness, I must make another batch of muscle ointment for Grandfather MacDuff."

Johnny worked most of the day to gather the ingredients. He really didn't mind for he liked to wander alone on the moors.

When he was finished, Mrs. Paul gave him another jar. "Here is the last of the ointment," she said. "Take it to Grandfather MacDuff, and mind you don't waste any of it."

Clutching the jar tightly, Johnny ran down the lane toward Arbigland.

He did not stop at the pier this time. He ran straight to his grandfather's shop. He stopped before the small stone building. Smoke from the forge billowed out of the low, narrow doorway. Johnny dashed inside.

Through the smoke he saw the tall, gaunt figure of his grandfather. He thrust the jar into strong, rough hands. "Here is ointment for your stiff muscles, Grandfather," he said.

Grandfather scolded gently, "You must not interrupt while I am speaking to a customer."

"I'm sorry, Grandfather," gulped Johnny. "I saw no one but you."

It was then that Johnny noticed his grandfather's customer. It was the Earl of Selkirk!

"I'm sorry, sir," he muttered.

"That's all right, young man," said the earl. "It is hard to see through this smoke."

"Hello, Johnny," said another voice. "Didn't you see me either?"

Johnny's heart sank. "There's that redheaded boy again!" he shuddered.

"Oh—er, hello, Thomas," Johnny replied.

Grandfather MacDuff was handing a musket to the earl. Johnny felt better. Thomas and the earl wouldn't be staying long.

Then Johnny saw his grandfather and the earl moving toward the door.

"Watch the shop for me, Johnny," said Grandfather. "His lordship and I will return soon."

"Yes, Grandfather." Johnny knew that he would have to stay until the two men returned.

Thomas seemed pleased. He went over to a suit of armor standing in a corner. The old gunsmith kept it as a symbol of his trade. Mr. MacDuff liked to be remembered for his skill as an armorer, even though he made little or no armor these days.

Thomas looked over the suit of armor. It was a full suit of plate armor. The plates were linked together so that the wearer's body would be completely covered. It was topped by a great helmet, with a visor that could be pulled down to cover the face completely.

"How could a man walk in a suit like that?" asked Thomas.

"It was hard," answered Johnny. "With some of this heavy armor on, a man had to be lifted onto his horse."

"Wonder how a man got into a suit like that?" asked Thomas.

"Like this, of course," said Johnny rather impatiently. He went toward the suit of armor.

Johnny tipped the top half of the armor forward. His grandfather had hinged it at the waist. The helmet, however, remained in place for Mr. MacDuff had screwed it there.

Johnny climbed into the bottom half of the

suit. It was a very uncomfortable suit. It had been made for someone with much longer legs than Johnny's.

"I wonder if you can see out of the helmet," Thomas inquired.

"Hey!" yelled Johnny, but it was too late. Thomas had tipped the top of the suit back into place. The catch snapped shut.

"Thomas, I'm locked inside. Do something! Hurry!" shouted Johnny.

Thomas fumbled with the lock. He didn't know how to work it. He couldn't understand Johnny's muffled directions.

"I'll get your grandfather, Johnny." Thomas called anxiously.

Johnny was left alone. He wasn't afraid, but he was uncomfortable. "It's best to be quiet," he thought. "My, it's stuffy in here." He could hardly breathe.

Suddenly he heard footsteps on the stone

floor of the shop. "Grandfather!" he called, but no one came to unfasten the lock. Instead he heard a strange voice growl, "Old MacDuff isn't here now."

"We can come back again. Say! Isn't old Selkirk going to be surprised tomorrow when he discovers that all the young trees he's been planting are gone?"

"Ha, ha! He will be indeed. He's mighty proud of that new grove, I hear."

"He won't be so proud tomorrow!"

The feet moved toward the door. Then they were gone.

Johnny huddled nervously inside the armor. That new grove of trees! He knew it so well. Why, he had helped his Uncle George set out the seedlings. "They are going to be torn up tonight," he moaned aloud.

"Oh, no, they aren't—not if I can help it!" he vowed. He would get word to the Earl of Selkirk somehow. "I'll have to get out of this suit of armor first, though."

He squirmed and wiggled. "Isn't Grandfather ever going to come? Where did that terrible boy go?"

Grandfather came back at last. He let Johnny out of the armor. "What happened, son?" Mr. MacDuff inquired.

"Oh, Grandfather! Something terrible is going to happen!" Johnny sputtered out the story of the visitors and what they had said.

"Goodness!" said Grandfather. "The earl has just left for the castle. We must try to warn him somehow."

"Uncle George will be coming home soon," said Johnny.

"Right you are," said Grandfather. "Hurry to the pier and tell Uncle George to row to the earl's island and warn his lordship of what is planned."

64

It was dark when Uncle George rowed his boat back to the Earl of Selkirk's island. Johnny went with him.

Johnny tingled. Excitement lay ahead! He loved excitement. He was certainly glad that his mother had let him come along.

The boat slid up on the shore of the island. He and Uncle George stepped out. They hurried toward the castle. Soon Uncle George was telling the earl about the coming raid on his young trees.

"Good," said the earl. "Now I'll catch them in the act. I'll find out who the rascals are, and punish them if they deserve it."

Johnny gulped. What would the earl do to these men? They might be friends and neighbors. Johnny didn't want to see them treated badly. Perhaps he should have kept quiet.

Johnny took one look at the earl's scowling

face. "Yes, perhaps I should have kept quiet," he thought to himself.

The earl, musket in hand, ran toward the grove with Johnny and Uncle George.

Johnny was happy about one thing. Thomas didn't come along.

They soon reached the grove. Not far away a boat scraped on the shore. Shadowy figures sneaked toward the grove.

Johnny's heart pounded. "What will the earl do? Will he shoot those men with his musket?" Johnny wondered.

The figures moved closer to the grove. The earl and his men could just make out the axes that the intruders were carrying.

"Halt!" cried the earl loudly. "I have a musket here and I know how to use it."

The strangers halted except one.

"Come back here!" shouted the earl. The running figure stopped.

"Now," said the earl as he stepped from the shadows and peered into the faces of the men, "tell me why you are so anxious to spoil my fine grove of trees."

"We don't want trees around here," growled one of the men. "They make people sick. They draw the dampness from the sea, and keep it here. The roots damage the soil."

"Trees draw birds," spoke up another man. "The birds will eat our grain. Your trees will ruin our crops."

"So you believe," the earl said not unkindly, "but you are wrong. Trees are a blessing, not a curse. They will not ruin your crops, nor will they make people sick. We need trees in this bleak land of ours. They will break the force of the wind and protect our fields from blasts and storms. Birds will come, yes. They will eat some of the grain, but they will also eat the insects that spoil so much grain now."

67

The men grumbled. They did not believe the
earl, and he knew they didn't.

"Perhaps," said the earl, "I have planted the
seed of a new idea in your minds. I hope it will

grow. You may go now. But remember," he said sternly, "if any of my trees are killed, I will know who probably did it. I know every single one of you."

Johnny knew every man of them, too. They were neighbors and friends. He was glad none of them was hurt. The men believed they were right in thinking the trees would hurt their crops. Now they knew better.

After the men had gone, the earl turned to Johnny. "I am grateful to you, lad," he said, "for bringing me this warning. Here is a reward." He poured a handful of shining coins into Johnny's hand.

"Thank you, sir," Johnny stammered. He thrust the coins into his pocket. He touched the sprig of white heather and grinned. "The heather has brought me good luck this time!" he beamed happily.

Hail to the King

It was the second day of February in the following year.

"Get up, sleepyhead!" cried Robert, giving his youngest brother a friendly poke. "You're a big boy now and going to school, remember?"

Johnny yawned sleepily.

"I hope Father wants us to go dig peat today," grumbled Robert. "I'd much rather dig peat than go to school."

"I don't." Johnny shivered into his clothes. "I'd rather go to school."

"You're a queer one," snorted Albert. "You like school."

70

Johnny liked school very much. He liked the old minister who taught school on weekdays. He preached in church on Sundays, too. The dominie, as the people in the village called the minister, was a kindly man. Johnny liked his lessons in reading and writing and religion. He liked singing hymns. He enjoyed the long walks to the church, or kirk, where school was held. In fact, Johnny liked everything about school except Thomas Selkirk.

"I'll fix old Thomas today," he thought gleefully, "He probably thinks he'll be king, but I'll bet he won't. I will."

Johnny stuffed his money, all the coins he had saved since last summer, into an old leather bag. With every shining coin he had put into that bag had gone a dream, a dream of the wonderful things he was going to buy with his money—a book of poetry for his mother, sweetmeats and treats for himself and Lisbeth and his brothers. Maybe he could even own a row-boat of his own one day, if he kept saving coins long enough.

Those dreams were forgotten now. Johnny was going to spend all of his money today. He was determined to show Thomas Selkirk that he could beat him at something.

Mr. Paul had no extra chores for the boys to do today. He wanted his sons to go to school. He kept them home only when he had to.

Johnny, Robert, and Albert picked up their lunches of oatcakes. They wrapped them in a napkin and stuffed them into their pockets.

"Here are your gifts for the dominie," said Mrs. Paul. "A shilling each." She gave each boy twelve coins.

Johnny grinned happily. It was just what he had expected. He put the twelve coins into his coat pocket.

"Good-by, Mother," he said, and left.

Johnny did not walk with his brothers. He chose a path which they never took to school. He liked to walk alone and dream. Today he dreamed of how he was going to get the best of Thomas Selkirk.

It was still dark on the moor at this time of the morning. It would be about sunrise when he reached the kirk. The wind whipped across the barren countryside. Johnny blew on his hands. He wrapped his old plaid closer about his shoulders and pulled his tam-o'-shanter down over his ears. Still he was cold.

He could feel the heavy lump of his copper-filled bag. He remembered what his mother had told him about spending money wisely.

"Be sure you're getting your money's worth," she had said. "Money so hard to earn should be spent with care."

Johnny chuckled. He'd be getting his money's worth today!

"Hello, Johnny!"

Johnny was close to the kirk now. He was glad for he was half frozen. He turned to see Charlie Burns staggering along behind him. Charlie's arms were full of peat.

"Hello, Charlie," Johnny answered. He took some of the brick-like chunks of peat from the other boy's arms. "I see we'll have a fire today. Let me help you."

They walked together. Johnny didn't mind walking this short distance with someone else.

Carrying the peat had been a hard task on such a cold day. Johnny knew that. He and Albert and Robert had brought peat to school the day before. Most of the boys paid part of their school fees that way. Some brought meal and some brought rushes for the floor.

Only Thomas Selkirk paid all his fees in cash.

Johnny and Charlie hurried inside the kirk.

The boys threw the peat on the hearth in front of the fireplace.

"Good morning, Johnny. Good morning, Charlie," Mr. McAlastair greeted them. The white-haired old dominie smiled at them kindly. He was seated on a bench which had been placed to one side of the hearth.

Sandy Hall came in. He dumped more peat on the pile. The children grinned for they knew that they would be fairly warm today. That wasn't always so however.

It took a great deal of peat to warm the big old building. Even though the windows were boarded up, wind still whistled through the cracks. By sitting as close to the fire as they could and wearing their coats the children could keep fairly comfortable. Even so, their fingers and toes got stiff.

There were no desks, just rough wooden benches arranged in a half circle before the fire.

No girls were in the classroom. Girls couldn't go to this school. If they wanted to learn to read and write, some kindhearted brother had to teach them. Such brothers were common, however, for most of the girls of the village could read and write.

"Good morning, Harry," Mr. McAlastair greeted another scholar. Though it was only seven o'clock, the dominie had been there for an hour. He did his best to warm the kirk before the boys arrived.

Two more boys came in carrying peat. They, too, put it on the hearth. Then they huddled with the others on the benches.

"Good morning, Master Selkirk," said the dominie. His voice held that extra politeness he saved for his only aristocratic scholar.

Thomas Selkirk came in wearing a warm greatcoat, its high collar turned up. With a warm scarf about his throat and sturdy boots on his feet, he was enjoying the cold. His red cheeks glowed. They made the pinched cheeks of some of the other boys look even thinner.

Thomas slid onto the bench beside Johnny.

"Hello, Johnny." He grinned as usual.

"Hello," Johnny said shortly. Johnny didn't like Thomas any better now than he had the first time they met.

Thomas tried to be friendly, but somehow he always seemed to rub Johnny the wrong way. Besides, his fine clothes contrasted too sharply with Johnny's rough ones. Money he never had to work for always jingled in his pocket. He was a young lord, and he was big for his age.

Johnny knew all this which didn't help matters one little bit.

When everyone was seated, an expectant hush fell over the room.

Mr. McAlastair cleared his throat. "As you all must know, today is Candlemas, or Gift Day," he said quietly. "Starting with Charlie Burns, on this end of the bench, I will call your names one by one."

Johnny knew all about Gift Day. Albert and Robert had told him. It was the day when all the scholars brought gifts to the dominie. The pupil bringing the largest gift was crowned king. Everyone expected Thomas Selkirk to be king today.

Johnny smiled, gleefully.

"Charlie Burns," said the dominie.

Charlie Burns rose. "Sixpence," he said, shamefacedly. He went forward to put the money into the dominie's hand.

The class sat silent. Most of them felt sorry for Charlie. His widowed mother had a hard time keeping her four children fed.

Johnny could see big holes in the dominie's boots. Mr. McAlastair needed money, but he did not like this way of getting it.

"Albert Paul."

Johnny's brother rose. "One shilling," he said as he stepped forward. He gave his twelve coins to the dominie.

"Very good!" said the dominie.

"Very good!" echoed the class.

One boy gave two shillings. The dominie's voice said, "Bravo!"

The class echoed him again.

Three larger gifts were greeted with cries of "Excellent!"

So on around the bench. Each boy was given praise in keeping with the size of his gift. Only Thomas and Johnny remained.

"Master Thomas Selkirk," said Mr. McAlastair. "It is your turn."

Thomas rose. "A half-guinea," he said.

A murmur of admiration passed among the boys sitting on the bench.

"Magnificent!" cried the dominie. Thomas

went forward to put the gold piece into the dominie's hand.

Johnny sighed in relief. Now he knew he would be king. He'd show Thomas Selkirk he could be better at something.

"John Paul," said the dominie. He smiled at the small, dark boy at the end of the bench.

Johnny rose. "A half-guinea and one shilling," he said proudly.

Every member of that class gasped. Such a gift from a Paul! A Paul had never been crowned king before.

"MAGNIFICENT!" cried Mr. McAlastair.

"MAGNIFICENT!" cried the class.

Johnny started toward the dominie. He thrust his hand into his pocket. It was his turn to gasp. The leather wallet containing his money was gone! He couldn't believe it.

Panic-stricken, he reached into another pocket, pulled out the twelve coins his mother

gave him. He put these into Mr. McAlastair's outstretched hand.

The dominie waited. Johnny searched again. No wallet could he find.

"I had a wallet with half a guinea in it," he said feebly. "I—I—I must have lost it." Red-faced, he turned to go back to his seat.

"The 'Magnificent' was misplaced," said Mr. McAlastair dryly.

A snicker rose. It grew louder and louder. Johnny wished the stone floor of the kirk would open up and swallow him. He sat down, fighting back tears of shame. Every boy was laughing at him, except Thomas Selkirk!

"I'll help you hunt for the wallet," said the redheaded boy. "At midday recess."

Johnny gulped. He had lost the coins in trying to best Thomas!

Thomas rose and went forward. Mr. McAlastair put a paper crown on his head.

"Hail to the king!" roared the class in honor of Thomas Selkirk.

And Johnny, to his own surprise, said, "Hail to the king," too.

HIS MONEY'S WORTH

It was a long morning for Johnny. It had taken him such a long time to save the money, and now it was gone.

"I will help you hunt for the money, Johnny," said Thomas. "Four eyes can look better than two," he declared.

"I wonder if Thomas *will* help me look for my wallet," Johnny thought.

"Where shall we look first, Johnny?"

Johnny's heart leaped. "Thomas! He *did* mean what he said about helping me!"

"The wallet must be somewhere between here and home," he replied. "It could be in any one of a hundred places," he thought as he recalled his morning's activities.

He and Thomas began their search immediately in the path outside the kirk. Some of the other boys saw them.

"Think you'll find all that money, Johnny Paul?" laughed one big boy. "As if you ever had half a guinea! Just big talk!"

"Trying to make everybody think you're rich!" jeered another.

Johnny did not answer. None of that mattered now. The one boy he had tried to impress was the only person willing to help him hunt for his lost money. "How silly the whole thing has been," he thought to himself.

But he did want to get those coins back. He would really put them to good use now.

Noontime passed. No wallet was found. "I'll help you hunt again after school, Johnny," promised Thomas.

A queer feeling came over Johnny. For the first time he almost liked Thomas Selkirk!

It was late when school let out. If the boys were going to find the wallet before dark, they would have to hurry.

Suddenly Thomas yelled, "Here it is, Johnny! Here's your wallet!"

"Oh!" he exclaimed. Johnny took the leather bag thankfully.

Thomas grinned. "Lucky we found it when we did. See how dark it is getting?"

Johnny grinned back. "And we're not fire-flies. We can't light our way home!"

The boys hurried to the village together. "Thomas isn't so bad," Johnny thought. "What if his grandpa is a lord? He can't help that. Besides, he *did* bring me good luck."

They passed a shop. Johnny remembered something he had seen there. He and Thomas went inside.

"That book of poetry, please," said Johnny. Johnny counted out the right number of coins. He tucked the book into his pocket.

He and Thomas stopped at the village bake-shop. Johnny bought two dried plum pies. He gave one to Thomas.

When they parted at the pier their faces were smeared. Their hands were sticky, too, but both boys were happy.

"See you tomorrow," said Thomas. A boat waited at the pier to take him to the castle.

Johnny walked home as happy as could be. He patted the wallet. There were still some coins in it. He patted the slim volume of poetry in his pocket and smiled as he thought how much his mother would love it. He smacked his lips, "That pie sure was good," he murmured. He remembered Thomas. Johnny suddenly realized that he had gained his first real friend.

Johnny's First Sail

It was a lovely Saturday morning in spring.
Johnny was headed for the pier to meet Thomas
Selkirk. They were going for a sail on the firth.
And he had his parents' consent!

Johnny wondered if he should pinch himself
to make sure he wasn't dreaming.

The whole thing had come as such a surprise.
"Grandpa gave me a sailboat," Thomas had said.
"It's a beauty. Will you go for a sail with me
tomorrow, Johnny?" he invited.

"Yes, you may go," Johnny's mother replied in
answer to his plea.

"It is good to see you friendly with a lad

your own age, son," his father remarked. "You spend too much time alone."

"A morning with Master Thomas will be a fine thing," Mr. Paul added. "You must learn to like being with other people. You'll be living with them all your life, you know."

Johnny was so surprised. He had expected a firm "No!" After all, the flax patch should be planted. A flax patch was very important to a Scottish family like the Pauls, because flax furnished the only cloth they had except for rough, homemade wool like Johnny's suit.

Also, the fields needed plowing and the byre needed to be cleaned. Peat should be dug and laid out in the sun to dry.

Even so, his parents had said that he might go sailing until midday.

"I'll catch a big, fat salmon!" he promised in a burst of thankfulness.

"It's the beginning of the spawning season,"

Mr. Paul replied. "The salmon are coming up the firth. You should be able to get one."

"Salmon!" Albert smacked his lips. "For a roasted salmon I'll gladly do your morning chores, Johnny."

"Johnny must do his own chores before he goes," Mrs. Paul said quietly. "You and Robert have plenty to do in the fields."

Johnny ate his breakfast hurriedly. He was tingling with anticipation.

With Lisbeth toddling after him, Johnny did all his chores. He milked the cow and took her to the pasture. The cow and sheep wouldn't need watching today for there were no crops yet for them to get into. However, there were some blades of new grass for them to nibble. These should taste good to the poor animals after being shut in the byre all winter.

Johnny fed the chickens. He gathered the eggs. Then he set off for the pier, whistling gaily.

Now he was on his way, with his fishing pole swung over his shoulder. He held an earthen jug filled with worms in his hand.

"Has it all been a dream?" he wondered. Johnny wasn't watching where he was going. He stubbed his bare toe on a rock in the lane.

"Ouch!" he yelled, dancing about on one foot. The pain faded. Johnny grinned and continued on his way. "No, I haven't been dreaming. That rock is real enough!"

THE LITTLE GIANT

Johnny finally reached the pier.

A brisk breeze was blowing. White popcorn clouds floated above the sparkling water. Sea gulls swooped in and out and around. "What a day for sailing!" Johnny murmured aloud.

Johnny looked about eagerly, but Thomas' sailboat was nowhere in sight.

Fishing boats were going out. There was Tom MacKenzie's yawl. What a bonny sight!

"I'll have a boat like that some day," Johnny promised himself. "And you can bet I won't be as sour as Old Tom. No, sirree. I'll be as jolly as can be."

Then he saw it—a white speck silhouetted against the grayish bulk of the Earl of Selkirk's island—the sail of Thomas' boat.

Johnny hoped that he could go to the Earl of Selkirk's island again soon. He'd help Uncle George and earn money, too. Before long there would be plenty of tasks about the estate which he could do.

The speck grew larger. Thomas waved. Johnny waved back. He liked Thomas now. They had been walking to the village together every afternoon since Candlemas. Johnny discovered that two boys together could have much more fun than one boy alone.

"I thought you said your parents wouldn't let you come," called Thomas a few minutes later, grinning broadly.

"I didn't think they would, but here I am," Johnny answered. "Your sailboat's a beauty."

Not much bigger than a rowboat, it had a mast and a three-cornered sail. It was painted bright red. On each side of the bow was painted the name "Little Giant."

Thomas grasped a post of the pier to steady the boat.

"How can it be little and a giant at the same time?" asked Johnny, laughing as he climbed into the sailboat.

Thomas smiled back. Johnny never liked him better. Thomas was wearing an old shirt and a pair of faded breeches, too. His feet were bare and his red hair blew wildly about his face. Johnny's own clothes seemed less shabby. Johnny didn't like feeling shabby all the time.

"It's little in size," answered Thomas, "but it acts like a giant."

Thomas pushed the tiller from him. The boat swung about. So did the sail and the heavy boom that held the sail at the bottom.

"Look out!" yelled Thomas.

Johnny sat down just in time. The boom, coming across the boat, missed his head by inches. When the sail was out far enough on the other side, Thomas kept it from going any farther by holding the rope fastened to the outer end of the boom. As the rope grew taut, a breeze filled the sail. The boat shot forward.

It seemed to be flying. Johnny turned his face forward. He liked the feel of salt spray in his face and the wind in his hair. A sense of wild freedom ran through him.

"Now do you see why I named my boat 'Little Giant,' Johnny?" cried Thomas.

He headed his boat into the little waves left

in the wake of a large fishing boat. Bravely the little boat rode the waves until they had spent themselves.

Johnny laughed with delight. Then he thought soberly that he and the little boat had something in common. They were both so small. "Do I act like a giant, too? I hope so," he thought.

"It's the easiest thing to steer," Thomas went on. He pushed the tiller one way. He pulled it the other. The boat answered even the smallest move of the tiller. It zigged and zagged.

Johnny wished he was at the tiller. The tiller was a wooden bar, like a long handle, that went over the back of the boat and fastened to the rudder. When Thomas moved the tiller one way, it turned the rudder the other way. If he wanted the boat to swing to the right he pulled the tiller to the left. Johnny wanted to try.

Thomas must have read his thoughts. "Want to steer it?" he asked generously.

Johnny took the tiller. The boat was easy to steer. It would turn on a coin.

Up the firth they sailed, past the Selkirk castle. Down the firth they went.

Johnny's spirits soared. At the tiller of the little boat, he was filled with a strange sense of power. He felt like a little giant himself.

The Signal

It was a beautiful balmy Saturday morning a few weeks later. Johnny and Thomas had risen very early that morning to go sailing again.

The boys had sailed down the firth, past the Paul cottage, almost to Whitehaven.

"Lugger coming in today," Thomas called out.

"Looks like it!" Johnny yelled back.

Johnny, too, had seen the white sheet spread over the haystack at the top of the hill. He knew that it was a signal for the lugger put out by the farmer who lived nearby.

The signal meant, "No English customs officers about. Safe to come in."

The men on the lugger would see the signal and go on to Arbigland without fear that the English would take the ship's cargo.

"I'm going to be a free trader when I grow up," said Thomas earnestly. "I'm going to own a lugger and bring my cargoes in right under the English noses."

Johnny laughed. "An earl's grandson growing up to be a free trader. Ha, ha!"

Of course, Johnny admired free traders. What Scotsman didn't? They were a bold and fearless lot, bringing in their luggers full of tea and spices and highly taxed luxuries, and selling them to the Scots tax-free.

How the Scots loved that! Though beaten by the English at the Battle of Culloden Moor, and ruled now by the English king, their spirit was not broken.

"We'll pay no taxes to the English king, if we don't have to." They would wink slyly.

So the luggers came and went, aided by the villagers on their way.

Back up the firth, past Arbigland, sailed the "Little Giant." The boys sailed for an hour. Then they stopped to fish. Thomas lowered the sail. He cast out the anchor.

Both boys put out lines. Soon, Johnny felt a tug at his line. "I have a bite," he cried. A big, reddish-silver fish with large black and red spots, leaped out of the water.

"A salmon!" cried Thomas. "A big one!"

He drew in his own line. He took hold of Johnny's pole. Together they pulled.

The fish put up a fight. It pulled and tugged and leaped. Once it almost pulled the boys over the side of the boat. Johnny thought surely the pole would snap. But the boys started to win. Slowly they started to pull the fish in.

Still it fought. It was close to the boat now.

"The gaff!" Johnny yelled. "Use it now."

He braced himself as Thomas let go of the pole. "Can I hold that fish until Thomas finishes it?" he wondered.

Thomas picked up the gaff, a long stick with an iron hook on one end. Leaning over the side of the boat, he struck. He speared the salmon and both boys pulled it in.

"Whew," said Johnny. "What a fish!"

"What a fight!" Thomas laughed.

They caught several more salmon, three big ones apiece.

"Mother will be glad to see these," said Johnny as they started back toward the pier.

"So will Cook," said Thomas. "But she'll most likely chase me out of the kitchen. I'm always getting into her cooky jar."

They reached the pier. Johnny got out of the boat. He didn't want to go, but it was almost midday. And Mother and Father had said he must be home by then.

"I've had a wonderful time today, Thomas," said Johnny. "Thank you for inviting me to go sailing with you."

"I hope we can go out again soon," replied Thomas eagerly. "Guess I'll get out and stretch my legs," he added.

Johnny looked back at the boat. If only he could take one more sail this morning. Just one more sail!

ONE MORE SAIL

The boys noticed three men on the pier.

The men were wearing waistcoats trimmed with braid, three-cornered hats, wigs, and shiny boots. No native of the village wore such clothes, even on Sunday.

"Customs officers," breathed Johnny.

"They'll catch that lugger coming in," whispered Thomas.

Then several English soldiers came into view. The officers must certainly have found out about that lugger! Thomas looked at Johnny. Johnny looked at Thomas.

"That sheet on the haystack! The lugger might be on its way. It isn't safe for it to come in now!" said Thomas.

"All the fishing boats are out. There is no one else to warm the trader of danger," replied Johnny. "There isn't a minute to lose!"

At the very same instant, both boys scrambled back into the boat. Two officers, striding proudly up and down the pier, paid no attention to the small boys.

Expertly Thomas hoisted sail. He turned the boat about. Down the firth they went.

It was then the little boat really lived up to its name. It skimmed down the firth with all the speed of a giant's seven-league boots.

Luck was with them. They met no lugger.

As they neared the well-remembered haystack, Thomas looked closely at the shore. He couldn't run the boat up to the bank. He went in as close as he could and lowered the sail. Down went the anchor.

"You stay here and keep watch, Thomas!" yelled Johnny, as he dived into the water and swam ashore.

Johnny knew the danger of what he was doing. If he were caught in the act of aiding a lugger, he could be sent to prison.

Yet Johnny went boldly on. Fear was no part of his make-up. Instead, the danger he knew he was running made his blood race and his spine tingle with excitement.

Once ashore, up the hill he ran. Closer and closer to the haystack he came. He reached it and yanked off the sheet.

"What do ye think ye're doing?" bellowed a gruff voice.

Johnny turned to face the angry farmer. He blurted out his story about the sudden arrival of the customs officers. The farmer cooled off.

"The lugger!" cried Johnny. "There she is."

In the distance he could see a two-masted vessel, unmistakably a lugger. The lugger hesitated. The captain must have seen the signal snatched from its usual place and realized the danger. Instead of entering the mouth of the firth, the captain set sail down the coast. He'd keep sailing up and down the coast until he saw another safe signal.

"Tell Jack McIntyre to let me know when the officers leave," the farmer told Johnny. "Most likely I can light a little bonfire here on the hill. Then the lugger can come in under cover of darkness."

"I'll tell Mr. McIntyre," said Johnny, as he ran back down the hill to the spot where Thomas and the "Little Giant" waited.

"If the lugger comes in tonight," said Johnny excitedly, "I'll get to help unload her. Father always helps unload the luggers that come in during the night."

"Grandpa does sometimes," said Thomas, "but he would never let me come."

Johnny looked at Thomas curiously. He noticed a note of sadness in Thomas' voice. "Maybe I have some things better than Thomas does after all," he thought to himself.

Back to the pier they headed.

Johnny didn't look back at the "Little Giant" when he got out this time. He went straight for Jack McIntyre.

Johnny had got that one more sail he had wished for. "What a sail it was!" he murmured.

The Bold One

"PUT THAT CANDLE over here, Johnny. I need more light," said Mr. Paul. "Get my awl. I must put new soles on Robert's boots tonight."

Johnny did as he was told.

"Are you going to put new soles on my boots, too, Father?" he asked.

Mr. Paul laid a piece of leather on the hearth. He set Robert's boots on the leather. With a piece of chalk he marked around them. With a sharp knife he cut out the new soles.

"Yes, I am," Mr. Paul replied. "On your boots I think I shall put two soles. You wear them out so fast."

Johnny grinned. It seemed he did wear out the soles of his boots much faster than either of his brothers did.

"It's because your legs are so short," Robert often teased. "You have to take so many steps to get anywhere. That's hard on boot soles."

Johnny didn't like that remark, though he knew it was true. He was almost nine years old. He was healthy and tanned, strong and wiry. Still he was small for his age.

Around the edges of the new soles, Father punched holes with the awl. The holes were close together and the same distance apart. A thin leather thong lay beside him. With this, Johnny knew that his father would sew the new sole to the old.

"Come on, Johnny," said Robert. "Let's have a game of spilikins."

Soon the boys were flat on their stomachs before the hearth.

It was an early spring evening of the year 1757. The Paul family was snugly gathered about a cheerful fire of peat.

Mother was spinning. It seemed she was always spinning. Any woolen yarn or cloth not needed for the family's clothes was traded or sold at the village fairs.

Johnny rolled out the handful of thin, colored sticks. The object of the game was to pick up the sticks, one by one, without moving the others.

He picked up the sticks that had rolled out the farthest. That was easy. Then he tried for those that were close together. Johnny was usually good at spilikins, but he wasn't tonight.

"That one moved!" cried Albert.

Johnny said nothing. He had seen the stick move. He counted the sticks he had picked up. "Not many," he thought. His brothers would beat him easily tonight.

Johnny's mind wasn't on spilikins. It was on

the coming pleasant weather ahead. Then he
would help Uncle George again. Then he would
earn more money.

He had helped Uncle George all last summer.

He had saved several coins, but he needed many more if he was going to get the sailboat he wanted, one just like Thomas'. Every time he sailed in the "Little Giant," the more he wanted a boat just like it.

"I can fish with a small net then." He threw out the spilikins. "I can catch more fish with a net than with a pole. I can dry them and sell them to the English. I can make a lot of money. Then when I'm a man grown I can buy a yawl like Tom MacKenzie's." The future looked bright in Johnny's dreams.

He was eager to start working for Uncle George again.

Johnny would go to school, too, when the weather was bad. The parish school held classes all summer, except for the two-week holiday of Whitsuntide. Some boys were often absent. Too many boys, like Johnny, had to stay home and work in the fields when the weather was good.

Johnny liked school. He liked to fish. He like to work for Uncle George, but he didn't like to work in the fields. He hoped that he would not have to work in the fields a single day this summer!

The door opened suddenly. A gust of dampness swept in. It curled back the warmth of the cozy fire.

"Uncle George!" cried Johnny in surprise. It wasn't often that Uncle George came visiting after supper.

Johnny ran to take Uncle George's plaid and tam-o'-shanter.

"Come close to the fire and warm yourself," urged Mr. Paul. He moved over to make room for his brother.

Mother stopped spinning. She made some tea.

"Ahhhhhhh," Uncle George sighed contentedly a few minutes later. "Nothing so cheering on a chilly night as a cup of hot tea."

Then he said calmly, "I have quit my job with the Earl of Selkirk."

"Quit your job!" The Pauls stared at their kinsman. Had he gone mad?

"Yes." Uncle George set down his empty cup. "I am going to America."

Mrs. Paul recovered first. "Then," she said, "you will see William and Janet and Mary?"

"I will," said Uncle George. He added, "I have missed them, too."

Mrs. Paul sighed happily. That would be next best to seeing her three older children herself.

It had been many years since her oldest son William had gone to America. William liked his new home so well that Janet and Mary had soon followed him. They were all married now and prosperous and happy.

"Going to America!" Johnny could hardly believe his ears.

It was late when the Pauls went to bed that

evening. Johnny was happy when he crawled beneath the covers, happy for Uncle George. "But how will I earn the money I need for my sailboat after he goes?" Johnny worried.

AFRAID OF A FROWN

"I hate to hoe and plant and pull weeds!" Johnny thought bitterly. "I hate it! I hate it!"

He had been busy at just such chores for two weeks now. Sunny weather had come. He couldn't go to school. He couldn't earn money. So he had to work in the fields. "I'll never get a sailboat this way. Hoe! Pull weeds! What a life!" Johnny grumbled. He was on his way to the turnip patch, to work all day.

That evening he was eating his supper gloomily when he heard his father say, "Tom MacKenzie is looking for a new boy to help him on his yawl." Mr. Paul turned to his youngest son. "If you can get that job, lad, you have my permission to take it."

Johnny's gloom vanished. His spirits soared. Fish from that bonny yawl and earn money at the same time. That would be living again, after all these weeks of hoeing.

Mr. Paul went on. "I hear he pays well, but he is a hard man to work for. Even if he does take you on, you will find him hard to please."

"No matter," thought Johnny. "I am going to get that job."

Next morning Johnny went to the pier. He was determined to get that job. He was going out in Tom MacKenzie's yawl.

Tom MacKenzie was on the pier. When Johnny was within a few feet of him, he saw a frown on the old man's face. His courage fled like a frightened rabbit.

"Guess I'll wait a minute before I ask him," he thought. He walked on past the old fisherman toward the end of the pier. Suddenly Johnny's courage returned. "I'll get that job easily," he vowed.

Johnny turned back. Mr. MacKenzie's frown seemed to have deepened. "Another minute or so won't hurt," thought Johnny. Again he walked past the old man.

A second time he started out on the pier. The frown was deeper, much deeper. Again he walked out to the end of the pier.

"Go back and ask for that job!" his common sense told him.

He went back, too late.

"I'll try ye," the old fisherman was saying gruffly to a big, strapping boy standing before him. "Get busy now."

Johnny just stood there. He couldn't believe it. He couldn't believe he had let such a chance slip through his fingers.

Afraid? He had never been afraid of real

116

dangers. But he was afraid a few moments before, afraid of an old man's frown.

Johnny's spirits sank like a stone in water. He didn't want to go back home. He didn't know what he did want to do. He stood for a moment, trying to decide. Then he turned and walked to the end of the pier.

He sat down, his shoulders hunched.

He didn't see the yawl go out. He wasn't looking. And besides, he couldn't have seen it through his tears.

He didn't see the "Little Giant" approach either, but he did hear Thomas shout, "Johnny! Want to go sailing?"

Johnny went. He knew he shouldn't go. He knew he should go home and help Albert and Robert, but he went sailing just the same.

Johnny and Thomas sailed and sailed. They sailed up and down the firth, into caves under rocky cliffs and into coves, hidden by steep banks. In one of these coves, at midday, they ate the oatcakes Thomas had brought.

The boys imagined they were pirates. They were free traders. They were gallant Scotsmen fighting the English. They raided the English shore. They brought back imaginary prisoners and lots of treasure and loot.

They were brave and bold and reckless.

Ha, ha. Something in the back of Johnny's mind kept laughing. "Bold and brave and reckless, eh? And just this morning you were afraid of a frown!"

It was late afternoon before Thomas and Johnny went back to the pier. Johnny knew that he would be punished when he got home, but somehow it didn't matter. He felt he had nothing more to lose.

Tom MacKenzie was shutting the door of his fishing shack when Johnny passed him. He heard the old fisherman growl to the big, strap-

ping boy, "Ye needn't come back tomorrow. I want a lad that'll work."

Johnny didn't hesitate this time. He walked right up to the old fisherman and asked, "Need a boy to help you, Mr. MacKenzie?"

The old man looked at him with a frown. It didn't hurt.

"Know anything about boats or fishing?" asked MacKenzie gruffly.

"I know a little about boats," said Johnny. "And I can fish with a pole."

Over his spectacles the old man peered down.

"Well," he snorted, "ye're truthful anyway. Most of these lads talk as though they had sailed the seas for fifty years." He looked Johnny over. "Ye're little, but I like the looks of ye. Be here tomorrow morning and I'll try ye."

Johnny ran all the way home.

"I'll never be afraid of a frown again."

A Lad That's Willin'

"You have the job, lad," said Mr. Paul the next morning, "but you still have to make good at it, you know."

Johnny nodded. "I know, Father." The other boy had lasted only one day. Johnny wondered how long he would last. "I'll have to work hard, extra hard," he thought, "to make up for what I lack in size."

Johnny hurried to the pier well before daylight. He hoped he'd be first at the shack.

"Morning," grunted Old Tom. He did not look up from the rope he was coiling.

Johnny was surprised to see Mr. MacKenzie

so early. "I'll really have to come early tomorrow to get here before Old Tom. That is, if I'm asked to come back tomorrow."

Johnny took one swift glance around the shack. Old Tom was neater than most fishermen. His two nets, neatly mended, hung on pegs on the wall. Several old sails were piled in a corner. Two gaffs hung on pegs. So did an old coat and a clean apron. A pair of high-topped boots stood beneath these on the floor.

In one corner stood a barrel almost full of salted cod. In another corner, on a clean cloth, were several stacks of dried herring.

The old fisherman pointed one finger at one of the nets. Johnny understood. He took the net from the pegs and started for the yawl.

The heavy weights dragged. Johnny's feet became tangled in the sagging net. He fell flat on his face.

Red-faced, Johnny jumped up. He looked back

to see that Old Tom was watching him closely, a frown on his face.

"Goodness," thought Johnny, "my fingers are all thumbs this morning."

He bent over, got a better grip on the net, and carried it aboard.

A few minutes later, Old Tom growled, "Are you ready?"

Johnny raced for the side of the boat. He jumped into it.

Old Tom frowned. "A boat is no place to run and jump," he said sternly. "Ye're not playing on the moor."

Johnny felt sheepish. He knew better.

The yawl was built much like Thomas' sailboat, only bigger. Two large, three-cornered sails went on its mainmast. A smaller sail on another mast farther back helped make the boat go and also made it easier to steer.

"Hoist the sails," Old Tom growled.

Johnny was glad that he had gone sailing in Thomas' boat. He knew just what to do.

From the belaying pin on the mast, he untied the rope that hoisted a sail. He tugged. Up came the sail. The pulley at the top of the mast made the pulling easier.

"Make fast!" roared Old Tom at the tiller.

Johnny started to coil the rope around the pin. It slipped through his fingers. Down came the sail with a bang.

Johnny bit his lip. "Will my fingers be all thumbs all day?" he muttered.

Johnny hoisted the sail again. This time he coiled the sheet about the pin and tied it so that it would not slip again. He hoisted the other sails, too.

The old fisherman's frown sent shivers down Johnny's back.

Then they were sailing down the firth. Johnny's doubts vanished. His spirits lifted.

124

"Will I be sailing in Tom MacKenzie's yawl tomorrow? Yes, I will."

He was determined to make his fingers act like fingers the rest of the day.

FISHING ALONG THE SEACOAST

On and on down the firth they sailed. They reached Whitehaven and went on past it. Old Tom was going to fish along the seacoast.

Fishing was best along the seacoast, especially for cod and herring. Salmon which was caught in the firth with pole and gaff was eaten mostly by the villagers.

Old Tom reached the place where he wanted to fish. Johnny lowered the sails. He threw out the anchor.

"The net," said Old Tom.

Johnny gathered up all the net this time. He didn't want to stumble again.

It was a pound net. A pound net is shaped like a pouch with a large mouth. In the center is a trap. Fish swim into the mouth of the net. They proceed deeper into the net until they become caught in the trap.

Johnny helped the old fisherman throw out the net. He almost went with it.

Old Tom said nothing. He just frowned.

The iron weights pulled one edge of the net down. Floats held the other edge up. This opened the mouth of the net.

Old Tom held one corner of the net. Johnny held the other.

"Pull her in," said Old Tom at last.

Johnny pulled on his side of the net. Old Tom pulled on his side, hand over hand, a few meshes at a time. Slowly, ever so slowly, they hauled in the net.

The net was heavy. "There must be a million fish in it," Johnny said.

126

"Don't count your catch till it's hauled in," Old Tom advised sourly.

Both the old man and the young boy hauled the net out of the water and up the side of the boat. There were a lot of squirming fish in the trap, but there weren't a million. The fish were dumped into the bottom of the boat.

"Hoist the sails!" Johnny hoisted the sails.

"Make everything fast!" Old Tom sat down at the tiller.

Then they made for the mouth of the firth. Up the firth they went, back to Arbigland.

Johnny had tried hard. He wondered if he had pleased Mr. MacKenzie. The old man's frowning face told Johnny nothing.

At noon Old Tom headed the boat toward home. Johnny ate his lunch as fast as he could. Then he ran all the way back to the pier.

All afternoon Johnny and Old Tom worked on the pier. Most of the time they spent cleaning the morning's catch of codfish. They threw the parts that were of no use into the water. The seagulls swooped down to eat.

Johnny had cleaned a good many fish for his mother. He knew just how cod should be cleaned. He knew that these fish should be split. He knew, too, that part of the backbone should be removed. Johnny's pile of clean cod grew rapidly.

Suddenly the knife slipped from his hand and fell into the water. He watched horrified as the silvery shadow disappeared into the water below. It was a good knife. And good fish knives cost a lot of money.

"I'll get it!" Johnny cried. He slipped out of his shirt and trousers and dived into the water. Johnny swam around and over the spot where the knife had sunk. "Is it hidden in the sandy bottom?" he wondered.

Then he saw the knife. He grabbed it. Up he went, leaving bubbles behind him.

Old Tom just sat there on the pier, frowning.

"The sun'll soon dry ye out," he said, as he and Johnny continued their task of cleaning fish. Sitting there in the warm sun, Johnny felt sad. He had made many blunders today. "I wonder what Old Tom thinks of me."

When the cod were cleaned, Johnny and the old fisherman laid them out on the hillside to dry. Old Tom had some fish from previous catches drying there, too. Johnny knew that it took several days for fish to dry completely.

Every day was like washday. Johnny understood that drying fish must be watched closely. The fish had to be brought in before nightfall, or if the weather looked like rain.

"Mmmm." Johnny sniffed. He liked the smell of drying fish in the air.

The herring was salted down in a barrel. The salt and water would soak into the flesh of the fish and keep it from spoiling.

129

"The boat needs cleaning," Old Tom said when they had finished salting the herring.

Johnny set about scouring the boat at once. Old Tom sat down to mend some of the tears in the fish net.

Evening was coming as Johnny started to bring in the drying fish. Worries were coming, too.

"Have I made good?" he worried. "Will Mr. MacKenzie ask me to come back?"

Johnny laid the last of the fish on a canvas inside the shack. Old Tom closed the door behind them.

"Put these fish out first thing in the morning," said the old fisherman. Then his gruff voice softened, ever so little. "Ye're little, but ye're quick and willin'. I like a lad that's willin' to work."

Johnny Changes His Mind

It was early Saturday morning, a week later. Johnny was wearing his best clothes. He waited on the pier for Old Tom. Today he and the old fisherman were taking their dried fish to the market in Whitehaven.

Johnny walked up and down the pier. In his mind he was already halfway to Whitehaven. He was the owner of this yawl, and he was taking his fish to market. He was spending the money he received for the fish.

"Give me a bolt of that," he was saying to a shopkeeper. "That Chinese silk would make a lovely dress for Mother."

"I'll take two of those," he said pointing to a row of dolls with china heads and painted hair. "I'll give them to Lisbeth."

There would be gifts for his father and brothers. And, though he wore a suit of finest broadcloth, he bought goods for another.

"Step lively!" Like pebbles against fragile glass, Old Tom's words shattered his dream.

Johnny stepped. He helped roll out the barrel of salted fish. He carried out bales of dried fish and helped stow them in the yawl.

He hoisted sails. He coiled ropes and made everything tidy. Then he sat down in the bow of the boat and went on with his dreaming.

It took him some time to spend his money. That was fun. He looked back at Old Tom, who was frowning. "I won't wear a frown when I take my fish to market," he vowed to himself. "I'll be as jolly as can be!"

Soon he and the old fisherman were in Whitehaven. Old Tom sold his fish. Johnny was surprised to learn that Old Tom didn't get much money for his fish—not nearly enough to buy a bolt of China silk, let alone all the other things Johnny had dreamed about.

Johnny and the old fisherman wandered along the waterfront.

There were ladies and gentlemen in rustling silks and fine broadcloths. There were servants and tradespeople in cheap woolen suits and worn homespun. Coarse shouts and rough words mixed with low laughter and quiet talk. The waterfront was a busy, noisy place. It was town, country, and sea all rolled into one spicy, exciting ball.

Johnny soaked up the sights and sounds and smells like a long-dry sponge.

A ship had just come in from the Orient. Sailors were coming ashore. Already merchants were pushing their way through the crowds, ready to bid on the ship's cargo of spices and silks and tea.

Another ship was making ready to put out to sea. "Going to America," one man said, "to Virginia." The ship had arrived two weeks before laden with tobacco. It was returning to America with silks and satins, fine woolens, china, toys and furniture. All these things were scarce in the colonies.

Johnny watched as casks of water were rolled up the gangplank. "Virginia! Some day perhaps I'll go to Virginia, too. It would be wonderful to see Uncle George and William and Janet and Mary again," he thought.

There were sailors on the waterfront, of course, all kinds. There were English sailors. There were Portuguese, Spanish, and French sailors. Some wore rings in their ears. Others had silk scarves wound about their oily hair. One had a noisy parrot perched on his shoulder.

Some of the sailors carried knives in their belts. Some were scarred and some were peg-legged. Strange-looking men they were, and mysterious. All of them walked with the same rolling gate of men of the sea.

"Do you s'pose any of those sailors are pi-rates?" asked Johnny.

"No doubt some of them are," Old Tom answered. "But they wouldn't be tellin' anybody about it."

Some of the sailors talked to Tom MacKenzie. Old Tom had once been a sailor himself.

The stories those sailors could tell! Of ship-wrecks and pirates and mountains of precious stones. They told about lands inhabited by painted savages. The sailors also described strange creatures they had seen living in the sea—creatures which few men had ever seen.

"On our last voyage," said a sailor with a patch over one eye, "I saw a school of mermaids."

"What's a mermaid?" asked Johnny.

The sailor squinted. "Funny-lookin' critters," he said, "half girl and half fish."

"Goodness!" said Johnny, thunderstruck.

"I saw a sea serpent," said another sailor, whose trousers were held up by a length of rope. "It was so big it could have capsized our boat with a flip of its tail."

For once Old Tom grinned. He had been to sea. He knew how much fun it was to flabbergast a landlubber with fantastic stories.

Johnny didn't grin. He was excited. "What a wonderful life a sailor must lead—adventure, excitement, faraway places, wealth!

"I don't want to be a fisherman now. I want to be a sailor," Johnny declared.

A greasy, evil-looking sailor passed by. The boy stared at him. Johnny wanted to be a sailor, but he never wanted to look like that.

Then Johnny saw a ship's officer. The officer was wearing a beautiful uniform. Gold braid shined on his chest and cap. Gold epaulettes broadened his shoulders and gold buttons marched in a row down the front of his jacket.

Johnny was impressed. "What a splendid figure he makes," he breathed as he stared at the officer in admiration.

"I want to go to sea. I want to be a ship's officer and wear a uniform just like that!" he declared vehemently.

A SAILOR'S LIFE IS A HARD LIFE

"I want no son of mine to go to sea," Mr. Paul said firmly. He turned to his youngest son. At the look of sadness on Johnny's face, Mr. Paul's voice softened. "A sailor's life is a hard life, lad."

"Life in Arbigland is hard, too, Father," Johnny protested.

"That is true," Mr. Paul answered, "but here

138

we are safe. In a storm we cannot be thrown into the sea. Pirates cannot attack us. We cannot be shipwrecked on a lonely isle where savages wait to kill and eat us. We gain only a bare living here, but we are safe."

Like a bitter pill Johnny swallowed each word. How different he and his father were! For in his veins ran the blood of his Highland ancestors, fierce and warlike.

Safe! Johnny didn't want to be safe. He'd trade all the safety in the world for one spine-tingling adventure! "How can I make Father understand?

"The sea is a hard master, lad," Old Tom said, when Johnny told the old fisherman of his desire to go to sea. Old Tom's usual frown deepened. "'Tis not all flying flags and bonny uniforms and coming into port. 'Tis also foul food and scurvy and the cat-o'-nine-tails. 'Tis scrubbing decks and climbing through the rigging like a monkey and sometimes fallin' and breakin' your back. 'Tis putting out to sea and maybe never coming back."

Johnny heard Old Tom out in silence.

Nothing anyone said could dim the shine on Johnny's dream. More trips to Whitehaven made the dream shine even brighter. The sight of ships coming in and going out again, the tales of sailors and travelers gave his dream a higher polish as the weeks and months went by. Its glow lighted Johnny's days and nights.

School took on new meaning for Johnny. In school he could get the education he learned he would need to become a good officer. On days when the weather was too bad for fishing, he went to school. He studied mathematics and Latin. He read every book on the sea and seamanship that he could find. An old compass, given to him by Grandfather MacDuff, was now his most prized possession.

Grandfather MacDuff did not make fun of Johnny's dream. Nor did he try to discourage him. Somehow the old Highlander understood Johnny's longing to sail beyond the distant horizon.

Thomas Selkirk did not scoff either. He and Johnny were still friends, although they weren't together much any more.

Fishing and school kept Johnny busy. Every day was a happy day for Johnny Paul. He and Old Tom were great friends. He had long since learned that the old fisherman's growl was much worse than his bite. Old Tom had formed a great liking for the small, dark boy who helped him. Johnny had always liked school. He liked it even better now.

When Old Tom found he couldn't change Johnny's mind about going to sea, he taught Johnny all he could.

"The sea is a hard master, lad," he said over

and over. "It takes brains as well as brawn to stand up to it, but I think ye'll make it. While ye're not exactly brawny, ye're wiry and tough. And ye have brains in good measure."

At the age of eleven Johnny Paul was still small and slender, but he was as strong as steel. Keen black eyes lighted a dark face. His movements were quick and graceful and sure.

"We must all cut down our dreams a little."

Johnny was determined to go to sea. He did not have his father's consent, but no matter, somehow he was going to sea. "I *will* go to sea, and I'll be a ship's officer, too."

Surprise Squall

It was two weeks before his twelfth birthday. Johnny was returning home from a day of fishing with Tom MacKenzie.

Johnny's mind was whirling round and round. He felt so bewildered. "What will I do? Will I have to give up my dream of going to sea?" he worried anxiously.

That morning Old Tom had said, "I'm gettin' too old for the life of a fisherman, lad. I'm sellin' my yawl as soon as I can find a buyer. I'll go to live with my daughter."

Old Tom's news had knocked the bottom out of Johnny's plans. When the old man sold his boat and moved away, Johnny knew that his fishing days would be over. None of the other boats needed a helper.

This was not the worst part of the fisherman's news. Johnny realized that his old friend would not be there much longer to teach him about sailors and the sea. Johnny would not be able to see the ships in the harbor at Whitehaven, or talk with the officers and sailors in the town.

"Just when Father was beginning to show interest in my plan," moaned Johnny, "this had to happen!"

"Going to sea as an officer might not be so bad," Mr. Paul had remarked.

Now Old Tom was going to sell his yawl. Johnny did not blame him for that. The old fisherman's health had been failing this past year. Yet Johnny wished they could have fished together just two more years!

Thomas Selkirk was leaving, too. "I am going to an academy in Edinburgh," he had told Johnny a few days before. Johnny had known that was coming. Boys with money did not end their education at the parish school.

Johnny continued to hope that he, too, would leave some day, to sail out into the world and become an officer. This dream somehow lessened Johnny's sadness at the thought of Thomas' leaving.

Now all these dreams seemed shattered. "I'll have to stay in Arbigland. I'll have to help Albert and Robert in the fields." Johnny felt like a caged bird, but what could he do?

Slowly he trudged toward the little stone cottage on the hill. Dusk had fallen. A faint flicker of light showed through the tiny window. Johnny had no way of knowing about the excitement that filled the inside of the cottage.

The moment he stepped inside the doorway,

his gloom disappeared. There by the fire sat Uncle George!

Mother was talking excitedly, "I heard a knock at the door. I thought it must be a beggar. I almost gave food to Uncle George."

Everyone laughed. A bag of food for Uncle George! He didn't look as if he needed food.

Uncle George's eyes twinkled. "I wanted my visit to be a surprise."

"Visit?" asked his brother. "Didn't you come back to stay?"

"Indeed not," replied Uncle George. "America is my home now, and to America I'll return."

Mrs. Paul spread the table for supper with her few pewter dishes, all she had.

A few weeks before Johnny had vowed, "Some day my mother will have nothing but pewter dishes. When I am a ship's officer, I shall have plenty of money to buy them." Now it looked as if he'd never be a ship's officer.

Uncle George's being there almost made him forget his troubles, but not quite. During the evening he told his uncle how much he wanted to go to sea.

"Ha," said Uncle George. "Perhaps I can help you. A shipowner I met aboard ship said he needed a lad for an apprentice seaman."

"An apprentice seaman!" Johnny had wanted to study and then go to sea as an officer.

"We must all cut down our dreams a little." Uncle George smiled at him. "You can still train to be an officer in the finest school there is—the school of experience. An apprentice seaman who has the will to work and study hard can rise to be a ship's officer."

Johnny grinned. He was glad there was more than one way to become a ship's officer!

"How can I get Father's consent?" he asked.

Uncle George's eyes twinkled. "Perhaps I can do something about that, too."

It was three weeks later. Johnny, heartbroken, stood on the pier at Arbigland.

Tom MacKenzie had sold his yawl. The buyer was coming for it at midday.

Johnny looked at the familiar, graceful lines of the little craft. Every moment aboard her had been happy. He hated to see her go!

Johnny felt that his days on salt water were ended for good. He'd never get that place as an apprentice seaman. Weeks had passed since Uncle George's visit.

"I could go to Whitehaven and get a job myself," Johnny thought, "but that would do no good. Father might give his consent to my shipping with a friend of Uncle George's, but he wouldn't otherwise."

Johnny was disappointed in Uncle George.

Uncle George was on the pier now. A strange man was walking with him.

148

Old Tom hobbled out of his shack. In his hand was a gaff. "I sold this gaff to Frank Kingston, Johnny," he said. "You know where he lives, down the firth a bit. I want ye to take it to him. I'll not be going because I don't feel too well this mornin'."

Johnny took the gaff from Old Tom. This would be his last trip aboard the yawl. He tried not to think about it.

Johnny noticed Mr. Paul standing on the bank. "Why is Father here?" he wondered, as he waved to Mr. Paul.

Soon the yawl was skimming down the firth. The old sense of joy and wild freedom surged through Johnny "For two pennies, I'd sail this yawl right out to sea," he thought.

He delivered the gaff to Mrs. Kingston and took the money. Old Tom was selling all his fishing gear, too. He knew that he would need every penny that he could get.

Johnny started back for Arbigland. Thinking about Old Tom, he did not see the squall coming up. Suddenly a gust of wind tore into the sails, almost tipping the boat.

Johnny noticed the dark clouds then. The gusts came even harder.

He lashed the tiller fast and ran to the main-mast. Working fast, he loosened the rope that held up the biggest sail. He started reefing the sail. Down, down it came. The wind whipped and lashed the sail, but Johnny wasn't frightened. He had been through squalls before.

Four men stood on the pier at Arbigland. They were watching the battle between the yawl and the howling wind.

"He'll never make it," said Mr. James Younger of Whitehaven.

"Oh, yes, he will," piped up Old Tom Mac-Kenzie. "Johnny has weathered many a worse squall than that one."

"You see, John." George Paul turned to his brother. "A boy who can handle a boat like that should go to sea if he wants to."

"You're right," Johnny's father admitted

slowly. "He'll not be happy until he does. He's more at home on water than on land."

Under Johnny's skillful handling, the yawl was soon alongside the pier. He stepped out and tied it up. Uncle George and the stranger and his father and Old Tom came up.

"You're just the lad I'm looking for!" said the stranger. "You'll make a fine apprentice sea-man, young man."

Johnny looked up in surprise.

"This is Mr. James Younger, Johnny," Uncle George said quickly. "He is the shipowner I was telling you about."

Johnny's father beamed. "His brig, the "Friendship," sails next week, lad," he said. "You may ship aboard her, if you like."

"I'm going to sea!" He took Uncle George's hands in his. He pumped them up and down. He danced about excitedly.

"I'm going to sea! I'm going to sea!" He said

it over and over as if trying to convince himself. He couldn't believe that his dream of going to sea was finally coming true.

Uncle George had done this for him. Johnny was sure that his uncle had planned this meeting between his father and the shipowner. That trip he took alone in the yawl had been arranged, too. Why, Frank Kingston was right there on the pier! He could have taken the gaff himself.

"Yes, I planned the whole thing," Uncle George admitted later. "Everything except the squall. That was a surprise," he chuckled. "It came at a nice time, though, didn't it?"

A Hard Master

"Good-by, John! Good Luck!" Young John Paul stood on the deck of the stout brig, the "Friendship." This was the happiest moment of his life. Yet, for some strange reason, there was a lump in his throat.

"Good-by!" he called back. He waved to his mother and father and Uncle George who stood on the dock below. His brothers and his sister Lisbeth had come to wish him luck, too.

"There's Old Tom, too," Johnny murmured. The lump in his throat grew bigger.

He was only twelve years old, but he was as strong and capable as a young man of sixteen.

154

At heart he was still a boy and he was leaving home for the first time!

The "Friendship" was going out with the tide. The 148-ton, two-masted, square-rigged vessel slowly slipped away from the pier. It was leaving Whitehaven, bound for Virginia.

James Younger, the owner, Richard Benson, the master, and John Paul, the master's apprentice were aboard with the crew.

Whitehaven, the Firth of Solway, and the coast of Scotland soon grew dim. They vanished from sight. A vast expanse of shimmering water was all the eye could see.

The lump in John's throat grew still larger. He was leaving behind home, country, and old friends. A strange new life stretched out before him. He was crossing the far horizon!

"Bring my long glass to me, lad!" The master spoke sharply.

John snapped to attention. "Aye,aye, sir!"

he cried as he ran to the master's cabin. He found the spyglass on the table and took it to Captain Benson at once.

At a respectful distance, John watched as the master opened the telescope. He pulled out several small tubes which were fitted inside the big outer tube until the glass was more than twice its original length. The captain raised the glass and looked through it with one eye at the sky line.

Suddenly he handed the spyglass to his apprentice and said good-naturedly, "Take your last look for a long time, lad."

John squinted through the tube. The coast of Scotland almost jumped toward him. The long glass made things look much closer than they really were.

John liked Captain Benson. He felt that the captain was a kind man. John was determined to please him in every way.

The first day out was an easy one. The wind was just right. It filled the sails and pushed the brig ahead with a swift, easy motion. Like a sharp knife the slender prow of the boat cut the water. A seething ribbon of foam, whipped up from under the rudder, was left behind.

The master paced the poop deck. This was the highest of the decks and was at the rear of the boat. It gave him a good view of all that went on below. He smiled, "If this weather holds, we'll make good time," he remarked.

Mr. Younger came out of his cabin several times. He seemed pleased, too.

John followed orders. He watched and listened carefully. Someday he intended to be a ship-master like Captain Benson.

John watched the man who steered the large vessel. The "Friendship" had a wheel for steering instead of a tiller. Close behind the wheel was the compass, on a stand called a binnacle.

The steersman kept an eye on the compass to be sure he was holding the ship straight on its course. There was even a lamp on the binnacle so he could see the compass at night.

The steersman liked John. He often let John take the wheel for a few minutes. John found that, by pulling the wheel around, he could make the ship turn. If he held it steady, the ship went straight ahead.

It was late afternoon of the first day out. For an hour or so a queer feeling had been creeping up on John. Now it caught him full force. He was sick!

Next morning he felt worse, much worse.

"Ohhhh!" he moaned. "I'm dying."

"Ha, ha!" laughed a seasoned old sailor. "Ye're seasick, that's all."

The others laughed, too.

John didn't think it was funny. He had never been so sick in his life. If he were home Mother would know just what remedy to give him. Mother! Home! They both seemed so far away! Suddenly John was homesick, too. "Why did I want to leave home in the first place? It's all been a big mistake," he groaned.

John couldn't eat. He couldn't sleep. He was really sick, seasick and homesick! After a while he got a little better. The ship seemed to roll less and he could drink a bit of broth.

Then a storm struck. A squall on the firth was but a gentle puff compared to this. The wind lashed and ripped and howled. Wave after violent wave pounded against the sides of the ship.

The brig, almost bare of sail now, tossed about like a cork. "Surely the brig will be smashed to bits," John thought worriedly.

One huge wave almost swept John into the sea, but he caught a spar just in time. He clung to it for dear life.

"Old Tom was right," Johnny thought to himself. "The sea is indeed a hard master. I wonder if I can stand up to it?"

Thirty-two days later the brig dropped anchor in the Rappahannock River. Not far away lay Fredericksburg and the home of his brother.

BROTHER WILLIAM

"Length of coat is about right," said John's brother William. He stroked his chin thoughtfully. "The sleeves are a bit long, though."

He went back to where John stood, stiff and uncomfortable, but happy.

In one hand William held a pincushion. In the other a pair of shears. About his neck hung a tape measure. He tucked up a half inch of the sleeves of John's new coat. He pinned wide cuffs over them.

"Fine," he said, pleased. "Fine."

160

John looked at himself in the mirror. He grinned. "What a difference a stylish coat makes! Why, I look as much the gentleman as Thomas Selkirk."

John strutted a little. "I'll never wear gray homespun again.

"Mother and Father won't know me in these clothes, William. Thanks so much for making me such a fine coat."

"I'm very happy to make a coat for my brother," smiled William.

The Paul brothers stood in William's prosperous tailoring shop in Fredericksburg. Bolts of fine woolens were stacked on shelves. Half-finished suits were hanging on racks, waiting for second fittings.

"The planters love fine clothes," William remarked. "They are willing to pay well for good tailoring. Here tailoring is a good trade."

"I think I shall stick to the sea," said John.

John was staying with William and his family in Fredericksburg. It would be several weeks before the "Friendship" would be unloaded and loaded again. Meanwhile he was making the most of his shore leave.

John loved Fredericksburg. Indeed, he was beginning to love the whole of Virginia. It was such a sunny, friendly place, very different from the bleak moors of Scotland.

John also visited with his sister Janet in Norfolk, and her watchmaker husband. He spent some time on the small plantation of his sister Mary and her husband.

John strolled about the cobblestone streets. In one shop he bought four pewter platters for his mother. In another he bought a book on navigation. He wasn't a ship's officer yet, but he'd study and work hard and some day he would be.

One evening word came that John was to go back to his ship the next day. The "Friendship" was to get part of its load for the return trip at Edenton, North Carolina.

William paced the floor while his wife packed John's clothes. "North Carolina is a little different from Virginia," he said. "It is a good thing you will have a chance to see it. How long are you going to be there?"

"About a week," John answered.

"I'll give you a letter to young Mr. Willie Jones. When he visited here I made some clothes for him. He was very friendly and I saw him often. He has a fine place near Edenton."

"I'd like to see it," said John.

"He will invite you up there, I am sure, if he is at home," said William.

USE MY NAME

The "Friendship" sailed to North Carolina with good winds. At Edenton, John found that

Willie Jones was in town on business. He gave William's letter to Mr. Jones, and sure enough, John was invited to visit his home which was located near the river.

The next morning Johnny had breakfast with Willie Jones at the inn. Soon afterward they climbed into a boat rowed by a dozen Negroes. The boat was very comfortable, with thick red velvet cushions on the seats.

Toward noon, when the boat was well up the river, they stopped to eat lunch in the shade of some trees leaning out over the water.

After they had finished eating, Willie Jones took out a snuffbox from his pocket. It was made of ivory. There were jewels on the lid. John watched in wonder as his host took a pinch of snuff with his thumb and finger. Just then the boat jerked. The little box flew out of Mr. Jones' hand, bounced on the side of the boat and fell into the water.

John gave a cry. He stripped off his shirt in an instant. Jumping to his feet, he dived off the back of the boat and swam quickly to the spot where the box had gone down. Suddenly John thought of the time he had dropped Old Tom's fish knife.

This time the water was brown. It was hard to see the bottom, but the water was not deep. John went down under the water. His breath was almost gone, when he saw a gleam of white. His fingers closed around the little ivory box.

John came up gasping. He was pulled into the boat, dripping wet.

"I'll get the cushions wet," he protested.

"That doesn't matter," Mr. Jones replied. He handed John a blanket to wrap around himself. "Remove those wet clothes and shoes."

Mr. Jones was rich. He would not have missed the box much if it had been lost. However, he admired John for thinking and acting so quickly.

He liked John better and better as the day wore on.

John stayed almost a week at Mr. Jones' estate, which was named the Grove. Mr. Jones had a race track there where he trained the fast horses in his big stable.

When it was time for John to go back to the "Friendship" Mr. Jones had his boat manned to row John back to Edenton. When he said good-by to John he gave his young guest some money for recovering his snuffbox.

"Thank you, sir. That is very kind of you, but I cannot accept," John replied.

"Well, thank you then," he replied. I know you have a brother in Virginia, but I would like you to think of me as part of your family. If you ever come back to America, I hope that you will come and stay with me."

"I'd like to come back some day," John answered. "I like America."

"I'm pretty well known," Mr. Jones said. "If you want to, just use my name."

John nodded. He didn't know it then, but the time would come when he would want to use Willie Jones' name.

The "Friendship" sailed the next day..

The return voyage to Scotland was a hard one. Storms tossed the brig around and the wind whistled in her rigging. There were calms when the sails hung limp and the boat stood still under a hot sun. Sometimes John was lonely. Sometimes the sight of water, nothing but water, almost drove him mad.

At last the brig docked at Whitehaven. John walked down the gangplank straight and sure of himself. He was a seaman now.

A Higher Goal

It was April 18, 1773. A warm sun was shining brightly on a small plantation along the banks of the Rappahannock River in Virginia.

How beautiful and green everything looked! The air was fresh and fragrant! It was spring, a time for gaiety and joy.

A young man wearing a naval uniform walked slowly to the top of a wooden hill. He was of medium height and rather slender. He held himself straight like an officer.

John saw none of the brightness and beauty about him. He felt none of the joy. His dark eyes were clouded with grief.

His brother, William, was dead.

John looked out over the beautiful rolling fields that were now his own. William had purchased the land, piece by piece, over a period of several years. Now William was gone.

The events of the last two days had happened so quickly. John was sad and confused.

It was only yesterday that his ship anchored in the nearby Rappahannock River. He went directly to the plantation.

John arrived to find that William was very ill with lung fever, or pneumonia. A few hours later, William died.

John Paul was now twenty-seven years old. John suddenly realized that he was now a plantation owner. "Today I became an American."

Inheritance of this land was the beginning of a new life for John. He decided that for this new life he should have a new name. It was then that John remembered what Willie Jones had said to him several years before. "I'm pretty well known. If you want to, just use my name," he offered. From that moment on John was known as John Paul Jones.

"What am I going to do with a plantation?" the new Mr. Jones asked himself. "I am a sea-man. I have never cared about farming before, and I don't care for it now.

"I could sell the plantation," he thought. However, John didn't really want to sell it for he loved the place. Since the deaths of his parents and his sister, Lisbeth, the plantation had been his only home. He knew the Negroes and liked them, especially the two boys named Cato and Scipio.

John wanted to keep the plantation, but he knew that if he did he would not be free to go to sea. He wanted to be free! He had to be free! The sea was his life.

Soon John was free. He discovered that old

171

Duncan MacBean, his brother's overseer, could run the plantation without help. So John decided to let the old man manage it for him.

For a while the new plantation master did just as he pleased. John hadn't been able to do that since his early boyhood days.

He spent much time on the sloop that belonged to the plantation. John and Cato and Scipio sailed in and around the rivers and shores of Virginia. John went to Williamsburg to attend meetings of the House of Burgesses. He heard Patrick Henry and Thomas Jefferson speak.

The more he saw of his new homeland, the better John liked it. He was leading a quiet, peaceful life. For a while he was satisfied.

"How pleasant it is to look back over the years! All my boyhood dreams have come true," he thought to himself. John was pleased with his life. He was now a ship's officer. He wore an officer's uniform. His friends were fine, well-educated people. Some of them were well-to-do, important people.

Now that John had reached all his boyhood goals, it was time to set another, higher goal. "What will it be?" he wondered.

"A planter's life when spent," he thought, "leaves no mark on the sands of time. My life must leave such a deep mark that the winds and rains of the years will not wipe it out.

"What is my destiny?" he mused. John was only marking time until his big chance came. In the meantime, he lived at the plantation. He sailed and fished and hunted.

Soon the colonists began to complain about the unfair way they were being treated by the King of England. John realized that war was coming. He listened and watched and waited.

Then came the Battle of Lexington! The colonies had decided to fight.

At once John realized that his chance had

come. "I shall make my mark fighting for my new homeland, but how? Where?"

John was a brilliant man. He was a good leader, he knew that. He was also one of the finest living seamen. He realized that he could serve his new homeland best on the sea.

"But America has no navy," he thought. "No matter! Everything must have a beginning, even a navy."

John lost no time. He wrote a letter to his good friend Joseph Hewes. He sent copies of the letter to Thomas Jefferson, Robert Morris, and Phillip Livingston. He offered to serve America in any position where his knowledge of ships would be useful.

John waited confidently for an answer.

He was happy. At long last John understood what his next goal would be. "I shall become a leader of this new nation," he declared. "That will be my higher goal."

Not long afterward an important-looking letter came to the plantation. John ripped it open. He was pleased to read:

"I have been authorized to invite you, John Paul Jones, Master Mariner, to lay before this Naval Committee such information and advice as may seem useful in helping this committee discharge its labors."

It was signed, Robert Morris.

Soon John set sail for Philadelphia with Cato and Scipio. "I am ready and eager to serve," he told the Naval Committee.

Mr. Morris was head of the naval committee. "We need answers to some very important questions. I want you to think over carefully what I am going to ask you. Then we would like for you to prepare a written report."

"First, what kind of men will be needed for officers? What about seamen? Must they be trained men?"

"I think I can answer those questions, sir," John replied.

Mr. Morris continued. "What kind of vessels do you think would serve us best? How should these ships be fitted for cruising work?"

"We will, of course, need several different sizes of ships for our purpose."

Mr. Morris leaned forward. "We have made you a member," he went on, "of a group of experts to look over certain ships anchored in the Delaware River. They have been offered for sale to the Congress. We should like to know if any of them are suitable for our needs."

"I shall be happy to work with this group," replied John. He knew full well the history-making importance of his task. He went to work with enthusiasm.

176

In a few days John handed in his report to the Naval Committee. He wrote down how much training a man would need for each job on a ship, from cabin boy to captain.

He listed the kinds of vessels which he thought would be of most use in the war on the seas. Also, he worked out a method for outfitting the ships. John outlined his ideas about what types of ships should be built, how many, and what size would be needed.

The Naval Committee accepted John's report with only a few changes.

The twenty ships in the Delaware River were were given a thorough going over. Congress purchased five of the vessels.

There was one large ship. It would soon be renamed the "Alfred." There were four smaller vessels. All of them needed to be repaired. The proper guns had to be mounted on each. John Paul Jones took charge of this work.

Months later the job was finished. John was very pleased with the results.

Five ships were ready to put to sea. This was indeed a small navy with which to battle the English fleet, the most powerful sea force afloat, but John wasn't worried.

"A small navy can beat a big one," he thought confidently, "if her commander knows how to make the most of what he has."

Commodore Esek Hopkins was placed in command of the new navy. John was made a first lieutenant to serve on the "Alfred."

Many people thought that John should have been made a captain, but the higher ranks were given to men who had served on colonial ships. John had served only on English ships with English crews.

He said, "I am here to serve the cause of freedom, not to push John Paul Jones ahead. I will cheerfully do my duty as first lieutenant under Captain Saltonstall. Time will make all things even."

On February 17, 1776, the first squadron of the new navy set out to sea. The cruise was no success. Its only battle was a running fight with the British sloop of war, "Glasgow." The "Glasgow" got the best of that engagement.

"We're running away from the enemy!" John cried. "Who ever won by running away?"

John had his own ideas about how a small navy should fight a large one. "I'd surprise and attack. I'd attack the enemy's ships, his seacoast, his towns. Surprise and attack!" he repeated. "That's the answer."

Since John Paul Jones was not in command of the navy he had to follow orders not give them. Nevertheless, he kept on making plans for fighting this war on the seas. "I'm not commander of this navy yet, but some day I will be," he vowed.

John's First
Command

On May 10, 1776, John Paul Jones received his
first command. He was made captain of the
"Providence."

The "Providence" was a small sloop of war.
Her crew was not large, nor were here guns very
heavy, but John was happy. He was in command! Now he could carry out his own plans
for fighting a war on the seas.

The seas through which the "Providence"
cruised were alive with British ships. All of
these ships were larger and much better armed
than the little sloop.

These handicaps did not worry John. He

knew how to make the most of the forces available to him.

"Surprise and attack!" That was his motto.

He moved like an angry wasp. He struck without warning and was gone before the enemy knew what had hit him!

Captain Jones captured ship after ship. The English roared, "Pirate!" The colonists gleefully sang:

> You have heard o' John Paul Jones?
> Have you not? Have you not?
> You have heard o' John Paul Jones?
> Have you not?"

Congress was highly pleased with John's many successes at sea. On July 14, 1777, a resolution was passed by Congress. It read:

Resolved, that the Flag of The Thirteen United States of America be Thirteen Stripes,

Alternate Red and White; That the Union be Thirteen Stars in a Blue Feild; Representing a New Constellation.

Resolved, That Captain John Paul Jones be Appointed to Command the Ship "Ranger."

"What a great honor!" cried John when he heard of the resolution.

He said, proudly, "That flag and I are twins. We cannot be parted in life or in death. So long as we can float, we shall float together. If we must sink, we shall go down as one!"

John was nearing his higher goal.

The "Ranger" was larger than the "Providence." For her, John planned bigger things.

"The English say their coast is safe, and that we dare not raid it. The 'Ranger' and I will will show them they are wrong," John said.

"Raid the coast of England with just one ship?" people asked in amazement.

"Certainly," John answered coolly. "Besides," he added, his dark eyes shining, "I want to be the first to carry the Stars and Stripes into European waters."

One midnight not long afterward, the "Ranger" anchored off the port of Whitehaven. Two small boats were lowered over her side. Into them went Captain Jones, three officers, and twenty-seven seamen.

Two forts guarded the mouth of the harbor. "We'll take those forts first, men," said Captain Jones.

The English guards did not see the Captain and his men until they had burst into the forts. "It's John Paul Jones!" they cried in terror. "He's raiding our coast."

John smiled. It pleased him to know that his fame had spread so far.

In the excitement one of the guards escaped. Quickly he spread the news: "A huge fleet of Yankee ships is attacking the town!" he cried, running through the streets.

The tiny raiding party headed for the harbor. Here the British ships lay at anchor.

"Set fire to as many of these ships as you can," Captain Jones ordered. "Do it quickly and as quietly as possible. We must take them by surprise if we are to be successful."

Soon several of the British ships were ablaze. Suddenly there were angry shouts from some of the townspeople, many of whom lined the shore in disbelief.

"It will soon be morning. We'd best get back to our ship," John chuckled, "before the townspeople discover that there are only thirty-one of us.

"Seaman, signal the rest of the men to return to the 'Ranger' at once."

The raid did little real damage, but it scared the wits out of the English. This was exactly

185

what Captain Jones had wanted. "Now the English won't know what to expect. Every moment they'll be wondering where we will strike next," he declared excitedly.

The British had mistakenly believed that no one would dare raid their coast or attack their towns, but John Paul Jones had dared. They would not soon forget this American man of courage and daring.

His Highest Goal

ON JUNE 19, 1779, Commodore John Paul Jones set sail from Lorient, France. He was in command of a squadron of four ships.

His flagship, on which he was sailing, came first. Called the "Bonhomme Richard," it had been given to him by the King of France.

The other ships were called the "Alliance," the "Pallas," and the "Vengeance."

At midnight the squadron rounded Flamborough Head off the English coast. It was met by a squadron of English ships, led by the frigate "Serapis."

The sea was smooth and a full moon was

shining. The sky was clear. Conditions were ideal for a night battle.

"A battle there will be," John declared.

The "Bonhomme Richard" engaged the "Serapis" in a fierce battle.

The "Serapis," a much larger ship than the "Richard," was manned by well-trained English seamen. The "Richard's" crew was made up mostly of volunteer seamen who had never been to sea. The "Serapis" was heavily armed, and there were only a few old guns on the "Richard" which the French no longer wanted.

In spite of all these drawbacks, Captain Jones was not worried. He had won battles like this one before. "I shall win this one, too," he vowed with confidence.

Suddenly a broadside squarely hit the gun room battery of the "Richard," and put it out of action. Now there were only the guns on her main deck.

Gun after gun on the "Richard" was crippled. The enemy's fire continued, as strong as ever.

Captain Jones strode about the deck, scornful of the bullets whistling about him. He shouted encouragement to his men. They fought on bravely.

Suddenly a hugh cannon ball tore into the hull of the "Richard."

"She's shipping water rapidly, sir," a seaman reported to Captain Jones.

"Man the pumps," he replied and strode on, deep in thought. As usual he was planning the battle as it progressed.

A company of marines was on the upper deck. The aim of their musket fire was deadly. "I must bring that fire into play," John thought to himself. "We'll have to be much closer to the 'Serapis' than we are now though."

"Swing about," he ordered.

Instantly the "Richard" swung about. Closer

and closer it came to the "Serapis." However, the captain of the "Serapis" guessed what strategy Captain Jones had in mind and ordered his crew to move her away.

The mainmast of the "Richard" crashed to the deck.

"The pumps are useless, Captain," shouted one of the seamen. "We're sinking fast."

The "Alliance" was drawing near the "Richard." Without warning she fired on her sister ship. John couldn't believe his eyes.

Through the din of battle came a cry from the commander of the "Serapis." "Do you give up?" he asked.

In a cool, clear, defiant voice came Captain Jones' fervent answer; "I have not yet begun to fight!"

Then it happened. The bowsprit of the "Serapis" swung across the deck of the "Richard." A dozen men jumped toward the bowsprit with ropes. "Lash her fast!" Captain Jones' triumphant order rang out.

Eager hands securely tied the two ships together. The "Serapis" could not fire her big guns at such quarters, John knew.

The tide of battle turned.

Captain Jones strode to the upper deck of his mortally wounded ship. "Fire!" he shouted.

The marines leveled their muskets. A withering fire swept the deck of the enemy ship. The English sailors fell back before it.

Desperately the English tried to free their ship from the "Richard." Every man who tried was met with a hail of bullets.

Under cover of the marines' gunfire, a band of Yankee sailors poured onto the decks of the "Serapis." The English commander pulled down his flag in surrender.

Victory came to the "Bonhomme Richard" as her deck was only six feet above the water.

"There is just time to transfer the men before she sinks," Captain Jones shouted.

On board the "Serapis," John watched the water close over his vessel. "What a gallant ship she was," he murmured sadly. "The only vessel in history to be sunk by the ship she conquered."

By 1787 the war was over. The colonies had their freedom.

High honors came to Captain Jones. Congress voted to give him a gold medal in recognition of his gallant deeds. He had served his adopted homeland with honor and without pay. He helped build the navy of a new strong nation. He led that navy to victory.

Now John Paul Jones was a happy man. He had reached his highest goal.

More About This Book

WHEN JOHN PAUL JONES LIVED

1747   JOHN PAUL JONES WAS BORN IN KIRKCUD-
BRIGHT, SCOTLAND, JULY 6.

King George II ruled Scotland.

The English defeated the Scots at Culloden,
1746.

Benjamin Franklin suggested a plan for uniting
the colonies, 1754.

1759   JOHN FIRST WENT TO SEA ABOARD THE "FRIEND-
SHIP" BOUND FOR VIRGINIA.

Patrick Henry attacked the Stamp Act, passed
by England, 1765.

The First Continental Congress met, 1774.

The "Boston Tea Party" took place, 1773.

1775   JONES RECEIVED A COMMISSION AS A LIEUTEN-
ANT IN THE CONTINENTAL NAVY.

The first battle of the Revolutionary War was
fought at Lexington, Massachusetts, 1775.

Patrick Henry delivered his famous "liberty or
death" speech, 1775.

1776   JONES TOOK COMMAND OF THE SLOOP "PROVI-
DENCE," MAY 10.

The Declaration of Independence was signed, 1776.

Nathan Hale was executed as a spy by the British, 1776.

The Continental Congress adopted the Stars and Stripes, 1777.

France recognized the independence of the thirteen colonies and signed a treaty of aid with Benjamin Franklin, 1778.

1779   CAPTAIN JONES ENGAGED THE BRITISH SLOOP
"SERAPIS" IN BATTLE OFF FLAMBOROUGH HEAD, ENGLAND, JUNE 19.

Cornwallis surrendered at Yorktown, 1781.

The peace treaty with England was signed, ending the Revolutionary War, 1783.

The Constitutional Convention met to frame the United States Constitution, 1787.

Virginia joined the Union, 1788.

George Washington became the first President, 1789.

194

1792. JOHN PAUL JONES DIED IN PARIS, FRANCE, JULY 18.

The population of the country was about 3,930,000.

Captain Robert Gray discovered the Columbia River, 1792.

There were fifteen states in the Union.

DO YOU REMEMBER?

1. When and where does this story take place?

2. Why did Johnny want to earn money and how did he manage to do it?

3. Why did he plant a potato seed beneath the knarled tree on the knoll?

4. Why were the villagers unhappy about the Earl of Selkirk's grove of trees?

5. What was the name of Thomas Selkirk's sailboat?

6. Which one of Johnny's classmates offered to help him look for his money and why was Johnny surprised?

7. How did Johnny and Thomas warn the lugger of danger?

8. Why did Johnny go to see Old Tom MacKenzie?

9. Why did Tom MacKenzie want Johnny to deliver a gaff to Mr. Kingston?

10. How old was Johnny when he first went to sea? Why was his father reluctant to let him go?

11. Why did John Paul change his name, and why did he select the name Jones?

12. How did John Paul Jones think a small navy should fight a large one? What was his motto?

13. What was Jones' real goal and how did he manage to achieve it?

14. How many ships were included in the first American navy?

15. What famous English ship did the "Bonhomme Richard" engage in battle off Flamborough Head? Who was victorious?

16. What was Captain Jones' now famous reply to the captain of the "Serapis"?

IT'S FUN TO LOOK UP THESE THINGS

1. What kind of place was Kirkcudbright, where John Paul Jones was born?

2. What were the duties of the British customs officers?

3. What were the chief reasons for the American Revolution?

4. How do present-day methods of preserving fish differ from methods used when John was a boy?

5. What are the leading types of sailboats? How do they differ from one another?

6. What famous battles besides those mentioned in the book did John Paul Jones fight?

7. Where were the following rivers mentioned in the book: Delaware, Rappahannock? Where were the following cities: Fredericksburg, Williamsburg, Edenton, Philadelphia?

INTERESTING THINGS YOU CAN DO

1. Tell a story about an exciting fishing experience you may have had.

2. Bring models or pictures of sailing ships to the class to make an exhibit.

3. Prepare a report about the founding of the United States Navy and the Naval Academy at Annapolis.

4. Go to a globe or a map of Great Britain and locate the Firth of Solway, Whitehaven, and Flamborough Head.

OTHER BOOKS YOU MAY ENJOY READING

American Revolution, The, Bruce Bliven, Jr. Trade
Edition, Random House. School Edition, Hale.

America Is Born, Gerald W. Johnson. Morrow.

First Book of the American Revolution, The, Richard
B. Morris. Watts.

George Washington, Leader of the People, Clara In-
gram Judson. Follett.

Patrick Henry: Boy Spokesman, Augusta Stevenson.
Trade and School Editions, Bobbs-Merrill.

Tales of Scottish Keeps and Castles, Elizabeth W.
Grierson. MacMillan.

Wonder Tales of Seas and Ships, Frances A. Carpen-
ter. Doubleday.

INTERESTING WORDS IN THIS BOOK

aristocratic (ă rĭs′tô krăt′ĭk) : belonging to the
upper classes

brig (brĭg) : square-rigged ship with two masts

cat-o'-nine-tails (kăt′ô nīn′tālz′) : whip used for
punishment in the navy, consisting of nine pieces
of knotted cord fastened to a handle

compass (kŭm′pȧs) : instrument for showing directions, consisting of a needle that points to the north magnetic pole

dominie (dŏm′ĭ nĭ) : schoolmaster in Scotland

epaulette (ĕp′ŏ lĕt) : ornament worn on the shoulder of a uniform

firth (fûrth) : narrow arm of the sea

heather (hĕth′ẽr) : low shrub which covers waste lands in Scotland

kirk (kûrk) : Scottish word meaning church

landlubber (lănd′lŭb′ẽr) : person who spends his life on land, person clumsy on ships

mainmast (mān′mȧst′) : principal mast of a ship used to support the mainsail.

mortally (môr′tăl ĭ) : fatally

mysterious (mĭs tēr′ĭ ŭs) : hard to explain

Orient (ō′rĭ ĕnt) : the East, usually includes Asia and countries east and southeast of the Mediterranean Sea

plaid (plăd) : long piece of woolen cloth, usually having a pattern of checks or stripes in many colors, worn about the shoulders by the Scottish Highlanders

pneumonia (nu mō′nǐ *a*) : disease in which the lungs are inflamed

poop deck (pōōp′ děk) : deck at the stern of a ship above the ordinary deck, often forming the roof of a cabin

reefing (rēf′ǐng) : reducing the size of a sail by rolling or folding up a part of it

rigging (rǐg′ǐng) : ropes and chains used to support and work the masts and sails on a ship

shipping (shǐp′ǐng) : taking in water over the sides of a ship

silhouetted (sǐl′ōō ět′ěd) : outlined against the sky

spyglass (spī′glȧs′) : small telescope

squadron (skwŏd′rŭn) : part of a naval fleet used for special service

tam-o'-shanter (tăm′ŏ shăn′tēr) : Scotch cap having a round, flat top and usually a tassel

tousled (tou′z'ld) : mussed, in disorder

Virginia (vẽr jǐn′yȧ) : Eastern State of the United States

wake (wāk) : track left behind a moving ship, trace or trail

yawl (yôl) : boat with a large mast near the bow and a small mast near the stern